Praise for **Mitre and Crook**

"Fr. Bryan Houghton's book is both hugely informative about the crisis in the Church that followed the Second Vatican Council and a deeply moving psychological study of the central character, Bishop Forester, in his struggle to respond to it. At a time when all seemed lost (and Fr Houghton was as acutely aware of this as anyone of his time), he was able to sow in his readers the seed of supernatural hope for the Church."

—**JOSEPH SHAW**, President, Latin Mass Society of England & Wales

"Published in 1979 by an English convert priest of 'gentry' family, *Mitre and Crook* has the sort of elegance people associate with a Waugh or a Knox, the deft humor of the satirist, and at times the helpless mirth of slapstick. There is insight into hypocrisies at every level of the clerical profession, and a prophetic picture of traditionalist seminaries bursting at the seams. But just as important is its acute portrayal of a decade when the disastrous inanities of Vatican-II-as-commonly-glossed were bedding down in the Church. Here we have that decade 'put on pause' for our leisurely contemplation. Lastly, we are served up serious arguments about the alleged 'prohibition' of the Old Mass—arguments which, after *Summorum Pontificum*, look remarkably prescient."

—**FR JOHN HUNWICKE**

"I read *Mitre and Crook* on a lark years ago and instantly fell in love: it is the best traditionalist fiction ever penned. Bryan Houghton was the Robert Hugh Benson of the postconciliar crisis. The author brilliantly portrays a bishop, of equal parts cleverness and courage, who orchestrates a complete restoration of Catholic tradition in his backwater diocese. Along the way we are treated (if I may use that word) to a positively scorching portrait of the souls of reformists, unbelievably narrow in mind and oblivious to spiritual realities."

—**PETER KWASNIEWSKI**, author of *Noble Beauty, Transcendent Holiness*

"An imaginative, boldly original novel about the crisis in the Church, the best book yet. Unlike so many explorations on this theme, Fr. Houghton's is a work of style and verve, more than a touch of wit, and deep feeling. It's a novel of sorts, in the Screwtape vein. You'll find yourself underlining on almost every page."

—**NEIL MCCAFFREY**, founder of Conservative Book Club and Arlington House Publishers

"All the erudition, wisdom, experience, and understated British humor of Father Bryan Houghton finds full expression in *Mitre and Crook*. Ingenious and absorbing, it proved invaluable to an earlier generation reeling from postconciliar chaos. Kudos to Angelico Press for making this inspirational testimony available to a new audience."

—**ROD PEAD**, Editor of *Christian Order*

Mitre & Crook

Mitre & Crook

BRYAN HOUGHTON

ANGELICO PRESS

CATHOLIC
TRADITIONALIST
CLASSICS

For information, address:
Angelico Press, Ltd.
169 Monitor St.
Brooklyn, NY 11222
www.angelicopress.com

978-1-62138-495-3 pbk
978-1-62138-496-0 cloth

Original book design
by Pat Slesarchik
Cover design
by Michael Schrauzer

Contents

5

CHAPTER 1

THE BOMB

Edmund Forester was born on April 2nd, 1910, the fourth of eight children, to humble and pious parents in a cottage in Roding Forest, where his father and forefathers before him were employed as woodsmen. Hence, doubtless, the surname.

After studying at the English College in Rome, he was ordained a priest in May 1935 and appointed curate first at Southend and later, in 1942, at Romford.

In 1947 he was made Parish Priest of Grumby and two years later became Assistant Diocesan Treasurer as well.

In 1956 he relinquished Grumby to become full-time treasurer.

In 1965 he was consecrated Bishop of Stamford, in spite of being suspected of traditionalism, because the finances of that diocese were thought to be in a parlous condition.

After Christmas it was customary for Bishop Forester to take a week's holiday at a secluded convent in Devonshire. Normally he invited his two friends, Canon Cocksedge and myself, to join him. We are very different men but he enjoyed the company of both. Sydney Oswald

Cocksedge, usually referred to as Socks, had been Bishop's Secretary to his predecessor and had remained Edmund's secretary for a year while showing him the ins and outs of the diocese. Edmund felt deeply indebted to him and appointed him Canon and Parish Priest of St Mary's, Sandborough, probably the most important parish in the diocese. He was competence incarnate, shrewd, very agreeable, ecclesiastically a bulwark of the Establishment but perhaps a trifle conceited and a bit cynical.

I had met Edmund by pure chance at some priestly conference during the early stages of the war, in the spring of 1941. We immediately hit it off and have remained close friends ever since, although I have never belonged to the same diocese as he. Unlike Cocksedge, I am an ecclesiastical write-off. I resigned my parish in November 1969 when the New Order of Mass came into force, and now live in the South of France. However, I usually return to England for Christmas and afterwards spend a few days with Edmund in Devonshire.

However, on Monday, January 10th, 1977, Edmund went down to the convent alone. He had put Socks off with some excuse or other and I had not come over to England. As soon as he arrived he asked for a typewriter. He had brought the stencils and duplicating paper with him in case the nuns ran out. He knew exactly what he wanted to say, so it did not take him long. In the meantime he got the nuns to write out the envelopes in their beautiful handwriting, which is about the only thing which has not changed in convents over the past few years. It was all finished by Thursday afternoon and he drove over to Exeter to hand in the odd three hundred envelopes at the main post office. He wanted to ensure their being delivered on Saturday morning.

As he drove back to the convent, he was conscious that he had not felt so happy for years—perhaps not since his day of ordination forty-two years before. He rang up his secretary at Bishop's House to say that he would be returning at 6 p.m. on Friday and should like to see the Vicar General, the Provost, and Administrator of the Cathedral, Canon Cocksedge and himself.

This is what Edmund Forester had written.

From the Right Reverend Edmund Forester, Bishop of Stamford.
Ad clerum 77-1.
Thursday, January 13th, 1977.

Right Reverend, Very Reverend and Reverend Fathers,

Since you are the priests of my diocese, it is in the first place to you that I owe some explanation for my actions and indication of my intentions. It is you who will have to implement and defend them. It is you who will suffer or gain because of them.

I have not consulted my colleagues in the episcopate nor the Apostolic Delegate. I shall send them by the present post a copy of this letter in order that they be duly informed. I am conscious that I am presenting both them and you with a *fait accompli*. Yes—but were I to act otherwise nothing would be accomplished at all. I prefer to have the arguments after the deed is done rather than before the deed is never done.

For some fifteen years now, Holy Church has been in a state of revolution. I need not tell you what harvest it has reaped: your own parochial returns are more eloquent than anything I can write. Throughout this period of turmoil you have shown wonderful obedience—you have remained at your post in near-heroic circumstances; you have continued to act as pastors to your flocks. At all events, the responsibility for the chaos and loss of souls is not yours but mine. You can find a ready excuse for whatever follies you may have committed. I have none.

Very well, since it is I who am responsible before God, I have decided that in the diocese which He has committed to my care the revolutionary process shall go no further. Indeed, by His grace and with your help, I hope to rebuild what has been so wantonly destroyed.

The revolution has two distinct facets: its method and its content. I wish to deal with the former.

The most striking feature of its method is that it proceeds by inserting the thin ends of countless wedges. It has never revealed its aim. None of us can picture the sort of Church it has in mind. Its ultimate objective has been hidden all along and, indeed, still is. Are the Sacrifice of the Mass and the Catholic priesthood to be abolished? Impossible! you may say, but you cannot be certain. Are infant Baptism, auricular Confession and the whole sacramental system to disappear? Perhaps you know; I don't. And what of "The One, Holy, Catholic and Apostolic Church"? It has already become "a pluralist, permissive, ecumenical and evolutionary ecclesial group." And then what? A World Religion? You do not know any more than I.

How many of you realized, when you stopped joining thumb and index after the Consecration, that you would be placing the Blessed Sacrament into the hands of the laity and that the laity would be distributing Holy Communion? And we know perfectly well that the process is not ended. I could fill a page with practices already in operation on the Continent and which will cross the Channel with the ease of migratory birds. Here are a few: the Sunday obligation changed from attendance at Mass to attendance at the Community Gathering; Eucharistic Meetings under lay chairmen with or without pre-consecrated hosts; inter-communion with non-Catholics (as is already allowed at Nuptial Masses); concelebration (i.e. when both parties consecrate both species) with non-Catholic Ministers; inter-celebration with non-Catholics (i.e. when the Catholic consecrates one species and the non-Catholic consecrates the other); shared tabernacles in shared churches; married priests; temporary priests— which we already have in view of the ease with which we can be laicized, etc... To date I have not heard of any lady-priests, but can any of you guarantee that I shall not be asked to ordain one? No matter what absurdity you think up, someone has already done it and soon under obedience you will be required to do it yourself.

The revolution is not concerned with doctrines but with "orientations," with our "outlook," just like a political party. Of old, we Catholics were a motley gang wonderfully unified internally, at the very core of our being, by a common Faith. We are still a motley gang but are expected to be unified by something extrinsic, by our outlook. All that is required of us is to tow (rather than toe) the line. But towing the line is a fruitless task if one does not know where one is going. Sooner or later one will have to draw the line instead; so it had better be done now in case it never is.

That is the basic trouble with the revolution: it hides its end but is adamant in its means.

Very well, my dear Fathers, I intend to do exactly the opposite. I wish to make my aim perfectly clear: it is to restore the Church very much as she was at the death of Pope Pius XII. This I know, of course, to be impossible in practice. All revolutions leave indelible scars even after the wounds have healed. Besides, some of the specific reforms may prove to have been beneficial, others innocuous; and time may mend still more far more effectively than could I. It is during the slow process of restoration that we shall best be able to appreciate what should be retained and what discarded. My aim, however, is clear and I shall not deceive you with edges of wedges.

A natural corollary of the "wedge" process is to have undermined the credibility of the clergy in general and of us bishops in particular. It is perfectly evident that we bishops have prescribed today what we proscribed yesterday and shall contradict tomorrow. It is so inevitable an element of the revolutionary process that I am doing it now in trying to get clear of the system! You have been expected to applaud the latest innovation while your hands were still sore from applauding the one before. Your presbyteries are bulging with literature which was obsolete before it was delivered. We have been worse than weathercocks. We have eaten our words so often that the laity think twice before swallowing what we utter. Was this what the revolution wanted, to undermine the credibility of the clergy? If so, it has succeeded beyond its wildest dreams.

Very well, my dear Fathers, I intend to reverse the process. After the honour of God, notably in the Blessed Sacrament, my first concern will be to save your faces, to restore your credibility. The point is that the honour of God is literally in your hands, since you are the Ministers of the Mass. Clearly, to ask you to swivel round again like the weathercocks which we have been, to clap and cheer as we have done over the past fifteen years, to tow the new line as we have towed the old will not restore your credibility. What will? It is by the *reality* of your Faith that you become credible. Not only are your parishioners not half-wits but often the more simple the more sensitive to their priests' sincerity.

What does this mean in practice? It means, in opposition to the revolutionary process, that I shall be far less concerned with your acts than with your Faith, far more with the validity of your ministrations than their licitness. Mind you, one of the most tragic victims of the revolution has been the Rule of Law, which it has substituted with the Anarchy of Whim. However, I am quite conscious that the Rule of Law will not be restored overnight. In the meantime I wish to leave you (always within the bounds of unquestionable validity) whatever liberty you can justify on the grounds that you would otherwise lose your credibility.

This brings me to a third characteristic of the revolution: it was wantonly unkind. Just think for a moment of the *Notification* of June 14th, 1971, which provided that the Immemorial Mass could only be said by sick and aged clergy with nobody present. These old priests had borne the burden of the day and the heat thereof. We all owe them an unrepayable debt of gratitude. What was their crime? It was their credibility: their love for the Mass impinged on the world of reality. But that is not where lay the greatest cruelty. This lay in the fact that no provision whatsoever was made for the laity who committed the same crime. They cannot say Mass themselves, nor indeed self-administer Extreme Unction and Viaticum no matter how sick and old. How easy it would have been to have allowed the Immemorial rites in Old Folks' Homes until, say, 1990! But no, the laity fail to figure in the pastoral preoccupations of the revolution.

It is true that in this diocese I did not go out of my way to persecute the few priests who clung to the old Mass. I also permitted the use of the English Indult whenever I was asked. But this scarcely exonerates me from being party to the basic cruelty of the revolution. These people had been robbed of an inalienable right. Did I do anything to defend them? Nothing! In fact, in my particular case the cruelty was aggravated by hypocrisy, since I said the old Mass whenever I could in my private chapel.

This last phenomenon is worth examining. I doubt if I am endowed with more built-in hypocrisy than my neighbour. How comes it then that I should prohibit publicly what I practiced privately? It is a result of the National Conference of Bishops: we had surrendered the personal rule of our dioceses to an impersonal committee. It is what Fr Houghton would cite as a striking example of the cleavage between the "collective" and the "individual" will. (See "The Talking Church" in the June 1975 number of *Christian Order*.) Anyway, you see the result. It is not edifying. It must stop.

Very well, my dear Fathers, I shall again reverse the process. I shall assume direct responsibility for the diocese which God has committed to my care. Of this responsibility the present letter is the first expression. Moreover, I shall not deal with the "young and healthy" as the revolution dealt with the "old and sick." A generation has grown up which never knew the pre-revolutionary Church. Priests have been ordained in and for the New Rite—and there is a contractual element here which should not be overlooked. Their divine vocation was, of course, to the Perennial Church but their human response can scarcely fail to have been coloured by their revolutionary formation with its outlook and ideals. They too have rights. I must be careful not to infringe on them, especially when I think them wrong.

Incidentally, at the moment we only have five clerical students for the diocese. At an early date I shall do my best to ensure that they receive the least inadequate formation available for their high calling.

That, my dear Fathers, will give you some idea as to what I find distasteful in the revolution and shall consequently endeavour to reverse.

I now come to the content of the revolution. It has affected every aspect of Catholic life down to the most ridiculous details. In due course I shall have to cover the lot. In the present letter I shall only deal with one small field, and that by no means exhaustively.

The first victim of the revolution, both in time and in importance, was the Mass. How shall I set about restoring it?

1. Concerning the Immemorial Mass, usually called the "Tridentine."

   a) As from today it may licitly be celebrated by all priests of this diocese.

   b) It should be said in Latin and using the old calendar; St. Joseph should be included in the *Communicantes*; the doxology *Per ipsum et cum ipso . . .* should be said aloud or sung, but not the *Libera nos . . .*; the Last Gospel may be said at the altar, as a recessional or as thanksgiving in the sacristy.

   c) In parishes with three or more Masses on Sundays and Holydays one of them (and preferably the High

Mass or *Missa Cantata*) should be in the Immemorial Rite.

d) I also hope that priests in such parishes who feel unable to celebrate the Immemorial Mass (which is perfectly understandable in those ordained since 1969) will arrange for an exchange of altars with a priest who is able and willing.

2. Concerning Eucharistic Forms promulgated after 1970, i.e. those for children, reconciliations and their derivatives: These are forbidden in this diocese, along with all personal innovations.

3. Concerning the *Novus Ordo*, promulgated in April 1969 and enforced in England and Wales on the 1st Sunday of Lent, 1970: This remains licit on the authority of the Holy See. It is intended for the vernacular and should not normally be celebrated in Latin. The new calendar should be used. I wish, however, to draw attention to the adaptations which I judge suitable for this diocese at this juncture.

a) The Ministry of the Word, Pre-Mass or Mass of Catechumens. This should be said facing the people from the ambo as you say it now.

b) The Bidding Prayers. These have led to some strange abuses. Items suggested by the mass media are unlikely to be news to God. I am, however, loath to suppress them at present. I suggest that they take the form of three Hail Marys for our Holy Father the Pope and the welfare of the Church. If the Creed is said, they would be better placed before than after it.

c) The Offertory. This is quite inadequate in the New Ordo and should be replaced by the prayers in the Tridentine Missal, of which I enclose an approved translation. At a vernacular Mass they should be said aloud and in English. I attach particular importance to the prayers at the Offertory. Why? Firstly, because the Mass is not only the making of the Blessed Sacrament by transubstantiation; it is also a sacrifice by the changing of the human oblation of bread and wine into the divine oblation of the Body and Blood of Christ. The Offertory is precisely the human oblation which is to undergo "trans-sacrification." Sec-

16

ondly, because the new Preces or Canons (especially Prex II) are sufficiently ambiguous to demand a formulation of the celebrant's intention. This intention is admirably expressed in the prayers of the Offertory.

That you all have the intention "to do what the Church does" I have not the slightest doubt. But in the turmoil of revolution, what goes without saying is much better said.

d) The Preces or Canons. All four are licit although I should have thought Prex II so obviously unworthy as to become obsolete.

e) The Consecration:
   i) At this point we are not speaking in our own names but *in persona Christi*. This momentous fact should be clearly indicated by speaking the words in a low voice and in Latin.
   ii) The words "*mysterium fidei*" should be restored in the consecration of the chalice.

f) The Acclamations. Those at present in use seem strangely inept. As an alternative I suggest that the priest, turning to the people and indicating the Blessed Sacrament, should say: "Behold the Mystery of Faith," and the people answer: "Thou art my Lord and my God."

g) Communion during Mass. Those physically able should receive Holy Communion kneeling. The Blessed Sacrament is to be placed directly on the tongue and not in the hand. Holy Communion is to be given only by priests and deacons.

h) After Communion, the priest shall purify the chalice and his fingers with the appropriate prayers, aloud and in English, from the old Missal. The two minutes' silence is unnecessary; it makes us appear to adore the Absence of our Redeemer rather than the True Presence.

4. A Hybrid Mass. Is such to be allowed in the diocese? Yes, I see no reason why the Pre-Mass, up to and excluding the Offertory, should not be said in alb and stole according to the New Ordo and calendar, facing the people from the ambo. The celebrant would then ascend the altar, don the chasuble and celebrate the Mass itself with his back

to the people and in Latin, according to the Immemorial Rite, up to and including his own Communion. For the Communion of the Faithful he could revert to the vernacular and, after purifying chalice and fingers, end the Mass according to the New Ordo.

In fact, I rather hope that this form of celebration will be fairly widely adopted. It has the merit of preserving the integrity of the Immemorial Mass while allowing for a positive contribution from the New Ordo. Besides, it may help to save our faces. We shall not directly and too obviously be denying what we have proclaimed. We shall rather be replacing in the new setting that pearl of great price which we had lost.

Fortunately in this diocese tabernacles have not been displaced and, even if the altar has been moved forward, it is still possible in most cases to say Mass with one's back to the people. The exceptions are known to me and can be dealt with privately.

There, my dear Fathers, that for the moment is probably as much as you will care to read, although, concerning the Mass alone, there are a dozen problems on which I have not touched. They can be solved as we go along.

You may well ask: what of all this is obligatory and what not? I only impose two obligations: Firstly, the prohibition contained in Section 2 concerning Eucharistic forms promulgated since 1970 and all personal innovations, which comes into effect as from next Sunday, January 16; secondly, the instruction contained in paragraph (h) of the section of the *Novus Ordo*, to wit: "Those physically able should receive Holy Communion kneeling. The Blessed Sacrament is to be placed directly on the tongue and not in the hand. Holy Communion is to be given only by priests and deacons." This will come into effect on Sunday, February 6th. All the rest is merely permissive; it is my wish and hope. Indeed, I have no intention of imposing any other obligation upon you until I have consulted the Chapter. Moreover, before I do so, I shall first want to feel your reaction, not by what you say but by what you do. This will take time. It is what you do which I hope eventually to make obligatory.

Am I making confusion worse confounded? Apparently, perhaps. A builder's yard often looks a mess. But you have an idea of my overall plan and I shall send you detailed drawings in due course. It will be up to you to build as best you can. Order will emerge as the building proceeds.

I have one further observation to make. The revolution has not just affected "this and that"; it has affected everything. It has not touched the dogmas of the Holy Faith but has attacked our attitude to all of them. It has undermined our piety; that is the basic tragedy. To restore the Church will not only require clarity in our aim and charity in our means but above all piety in our persons. Granted this, God will rebuild it for us.

Although this is an *Ad clerum* rather than a Pastoral Letter, I direct that it should be read or explained in your own words to the faithful of the diocese at all public masses on Sunday, January 16th, 1977.

⁎Edmund, Bishop of Stamford.

◇　◇　◇

On Friday Edmund got back to Bishop's House punctually at 6 p.m. He had pulled into a carpark so as not to arrive too soon. He found the reverend gentlemen duly waiting for him in the sitting room. After a few pleasantries he asked his admirable secretary, one Herbert FitzHenry, to pass stiff drinks all round as they would probably need them. He then handed them a copy of the Ad clerum *and asked them to make no comments until they had all read it. This seemed to take an age, especially as the Provost is not a fast reader.*

Their reactions, *Edmund wrote to me*, were exactly what I had expected: they corresponded to their personal characters and had very little to do with my Bomb. The Vicar General was enthusiastic and flapped; Socks was unenthusiastic and did not; the Provost, after such unusual concentration, was assailed by an uncontrollable fit of yawning; the Administrator, a keen musician who could not care less about religion so long as the music is all right, thought the document meaningless as there was no indication as to when plain chant or polyphony was to be used. Fitz made a sensible remark: "It required much courage to write but will need even more hard work to see it through."

I explained what I wanted each of them to do. The Vicar General would run the diocese without my interference, except for matters arising from the Bomb. The Provost was to call a meeting of the Chapter and make the Canons happy. The Administrator was to arrange for me to say a Pontifical High Mass according to the Old Rite at 11 o'clock on Sunday in the Cathedral. He was to send a curate over the weekend to Sandborough to supply for Socks. Finally—which made him willing to do anything—he was to draw up a memorandum on what was musically desirable in view of the new look. Socks was to man the telephone. I am not to be available to anybody on that infernal instrument, be it the Pope in person. Moreover, appointments should be given to nobody except to priests of the diocese, who have a right to see their bishop. This will force people to write—and they are likely to be far more circumspect on paper than they might be by word of mouth. Fitz and I will deal with the correspondence. However, after the first excitement, the phone will obviously diminish and the correspondence increase; Socks will then be able to transfer from the former to the latter to help Fitz out.

The press would clearly get to know, perhaps on Saturday, certainly on Sunday. I was not to be interviewed by individual correspondents but was willing to give three press conferences. The first to the Catholic Press, to whom I had sent copies of the Bomb from Exeter. The second to the locals, daily and weekly, for whom I have a soft spot. The third to the nationals. Journalists being what they are, the latter would infallibly ring up after the conference to get a particular line of their own: what is my attitude to women's rights, vivisection, vandalism, life on Mars, racialism and the rest. Socks was to keep them firmly at bay.

Today (Saturday) has been a day of waiting. The phone has rung constantly and Socks has brought me notes on the calls. There were sixteen calls from diocesan priests—which is rather fewer than I had expected. Of these, twelve were in enthusiastic support. Two had qualms of conscience as to what the Pope might say about it. One—but he is a surly devil anyway—wanted to assure me that he would say Mass as he liked, and one asked to be excardinated immediately to any diocese where the bishop was certifiable as sane. Actually, the last chap is a very good priest; he has unfortunately got into the habit of talking before he thinks; he will come round all right.

There were eight calls from bishops, of whom one, believe it or not, said he was in complete agreement and would follow suit. He was old Charlie of Birkenhead. I can scarcely believe it. If the rot sets in on the Bench, willy-nilly the whole lot are bound to collapse. Do you know Charlie? He is a sweet, good man, as totally devoid of guts as he is of malice. But then, God can choose what instruments He likes. The seven others, according to Socks, sounded agreeable enough but were noncommittal when they could not get hold of me.

There were two calls from the Apostolic Delegation, both from the Counsellor, that comic little fellow Mgr Testastorta. I rather presume that the Delegate has done a diplomatic bunk. Anyway, having failed to get through to me on the first call, he rang again for an appointment. When this was refused he used quite undiplomatic language, which has increased a hundredfold Sock's vocabulary of Italian expletives. I shall doubtless hear more from that source.

The Administrator has been popping in almost as frequently as Socks to settle details about the Pontifical High Mass tomorrow. I have not dared tell him that it will be the first time that I shall have celebrated one myself. I was only consecrated in '65, by which time we already had the vernacular mumbo-jumbo and the Punch-and-Judy show of concelebration. Naturally I agreed to whatever he suggested as I knew no better. I have gained an important ally there as he is highly respected in the diocese. But just think of it, Bryan: I have been a bishop for twelve years but have never said a Pontifical High Mass in the Immemorial Rite.

So Saturday is over. I enclose a copy of the Bomb. I write all this nonsense in order to relieve the pressure. It is already 1 a.m. and I must try to sleep—although I doubt if I shall.

I hope to write to you once a week, on Saturday or Sunday, to keep you up to date.

I am desperately happy in my soul although desperately tired in my body.

God bless you—and say a Mass for me, you who have never sullied your soul with a Eucharistic picnic.

It is from this long letter, overexcited, overwrought as it is, that I know the details concerning the production of the Bomb.

CHAPTER TWO

THE BLAST

I do not possess copies of the letters addressed to Bishop Forester but only of his replies. How these came into my possession will be seen in due course.

It is a vast correspondence. To publish it all is out of the question; besides, much of it is by its nature repetitive. I have consequently selected those which either vindicate my friend or seem to me to be of general interest. In the present chapter I give letters written by him between Monday, January 17th, and Saturday, January 22nd, 1977. I have divided them into those addressed to his fellow bishops and the Delegate's office; those addressed to clergy; and finally those to the laity.

LETTERS ADDRESSED TO BISHOPS

1. To the Cardinal.
Monday, January 17th, 1977.

My Lord Cardinal,
   I am most grateful for your little note.
   "Your heart" you say, "is with me although your head is not." This is far more than I had dared to hope.

Incidentally, have you ever noticed that in Holy Writ God constantly refers to Himself as *"scrutator cordis"** but only twice have I noticed that He calls Himself *"scrutator mentis."***

Yes, I shall keep you informed of developments—although I may have to ask for your discretion.

I well realize that I am in for a tough time but it will certainly soften many a blow to know that it does not proceed from you.

Your obedient servant in Dmno,

◇ ◇ ◇

2.   To Monsignor Tarquinio Testastorta,
Chancellor at the Apostolic Delegation.
Monday, January 17th, 1977.

Dear Monsignor Testastorta,

I notice that, during the absence of the Delegate, it is you who are running the Delegation as usual.

I am delighted to have from so authoritative a source as yourself that "it is not the Latin Mass, even in its Tridentine form, which is at issue." Such being the happy case, I fail to understand the logic behind the continuation of your sentence: "but that it should be used as the focal point for resistance to the decrees of the Council and the ensuing reforms." If the Immemorial Mass is not itself an issue, then it cannot possibly be the focal point for what is—unless, of course, you choose to make it so.

I also deny that my action is in any way "divisive." On the contrary, what I have done is to scrape off a bit of the wallpaper in order to put some cement into the cracks.

You say that you will make everything easy for me, both here and in Rome, if I undertake now to withdraw my *Ad clerum* "at a convenient time, say after the Low Week Meeting, when its failure will have become apparent to all." I assure you that I shall indeed withdraw it as soon as "its failure has become apparent to all" but not a minute before. In spite of which I feel sure that you will nonetheless do all

*the examiner of hearts
**the examiner of minds

in your power to make everything easy both here and in Rome for

Your obedient servant in Dmno,

◇   ◇   ◇

3.   To Charles Blythe, Bishop of Birkenhead.
Monday, January 17th, 1977.

Dear Charles,

I was told about your telephone call on Saturday. It is simply wonderful—beyond my highest hopes and wildest dreams. I could be ignored and eventually squashed but not you and certainly not both of us. The battle is in practice won although only one shot has been fired.

No, I do not expect you to come out with a fanfare of trumpets this weekend—although it might well precipitate a very desirable avalanche. I understand perfectly your feeling that a little preparation is necessary. I myself took none. But this is largely a question of character: some prefer to plunge into the deep, others to wet their toes and gradually sink into the cleansing waters. It is cleansing, incidentally: I have never felt so clean since the day of my ordination.

As a matter of fact, I myself had thought of doing very much what you propose to do. I intended to delegate all Deans to give permission for the use of Heenan's Indult upon request. I decided against because it would be likely to cause the abolition of the Indult. If this were done, then my present action would appear directly provocative. But this no longer applies since I have exploded my bomb. Your use of the Indult will appear to be a statesmanlike compromise or, at least, the lesser of two evils.

However, you are as well aware as I of the immense pressure from Rome for us to petition the Holy See to abolish the Indult. How devious can one get? Rome will not abolish it honestly: it wants to look goody-goody. It is we who are expected to look the knaves. I was not at the Hierarchy's meeting last August because I was in the hospital; but you were there. You know that there were plenty of the brethren, led by . . . and . . ., who were only too willing to oblige. In fact it was decided to "phase it out." This would have happened had it not been for a very few honest fellows like yourself who could not see how a permission is to be "phased out":

25

either you give it or you do not; you cannot ¾ give it, then ½, then ¼ and so on.

I remind you of all this because you must be prepared for the abolition of the Indult. It is then that you will have to come out with the fanfare of trumpets. In fact, if Testastorta gets in touch with you (which he certainly will) then I make so bold as to suggest that you tell him straight: so long as the Indult exists you will use it to its utmost limit; if it is abolished you will go "rogue" like the wild beast from Stamford. It is a terrible thing to say, Charles, but blackmail is the only language which revolutionaries talk and understand.

The last couple of paragraphs I believe to be rather important. You see, I think that you can save the Indult. Now it is clear that far more of the brethren are likely to follow you than me and your seeming compromise rather than my apparent defiance. The only snag is that Testastorta is no fool: if a chump like me can see it, so can he. What will be the result? The Indult will be abolished without waiting for any humble petition from us. Either way, polish your trumpets, Charles, polish your trumpets.

There is so much more which I should like to say but there are stacks of letters to be answered.

Thank you, Charles,

And may God bless both of us.

◇   ◇   ◇

4.   To Philip Goodman, Bishop of Hull.
Monday, January 17th, 1977.

Dear Philip,

It is extraordinary, you know, how images, metaphors, colour our judgments. I am by no means certain that Christians ought to be "outward- and forward-looking." I even wonder if you really are. It seems to me that we cannot help being downward- and upward-looking: downward into the abyss of our own void and upward into the abyss of the Absolute Being. Herein lies the difference between the new horizontal and anthropocentric outlook as against the old vertical and theocentric religion. The one is precisely an outlook and the other precisely a religion: they have nothing in common. Moreover, I need scarcely remind you that, no matter how

26

"forward-looking" one may be, one still has to look forward to death. What a wonderful and splendid thing death is: the punishment for sin turned by an omnipotent hand into the means of being grasped by God! I wish priests would preach more about death. Perhaps they do not believe in it any more? They used to say "black Masses" a bit too often, perhaps; now, of course, they say none at all. You who are an expert on the Council documents, did Vatican II abolish death along with Friday fish? It would doubtless be in *Gaudium et Spes*: I have never read it as I use it as a remedy against insomnia.

Excuse me, Philip, I am being flippant; but flippancy, as you know, is my signature tune.

However that may be, I cannot sufficiently express my gratitude for your remark: "I disagree entirely with what you have done but shall maintain through thick and thin that you have the right to do it." Nobly said, my dear Philip! What more could I conceivably ask of you? You are willing to give me a fair trial.

As a matter of fact one of my principal criticisms at the practical level of the New Eucharist is that it was never given a trial run. Do you remember the great Ground Nut Scheme shortly after the war, when millions and millions of £s were ploughed into the virgin forests of Africa for never a nut? No need for a pilot run: all the *periti* knew that it would work. Unfortunately, the nuts thought otherwise. The New Religion is just the same. Endless dialogues, conferences, planning, fervour, enthusiasm, renewal, do-gooding have been ploughed into the faithful. It has produced nothing but empty churches. Any industrialist who wished to market a brand new product would go to some trouble to ascertain consumer reaction. Not so Holy Church. And the fact is that the consumer, the laity, think that what they have been given is cheap trash. The clergy can dress up as commercial travellers to their heart's content but nobody is even remotely interested in the goods they flog.

What I am really getting at is this: provided the Brethren do not shoot me down too sharply, the poor little diocese of Stamford can become the trial ground for consumer reaction to the Immemorial Religion. That is where a man of your standing and acknowledged integrity can be so important. I do not expect you to follow me—as yet: I beg and pray that you exert all your influence to ensure a fair trial at Stamford.

27

As you say, mine is a daunting task. But I intend to carry it through, come what may. That is why I beg for your prayers as well as your benevolence.

◇　◇　◇

5.　To Stephen O'Keary, Bishop of Devizes.
Monday January 17th, 1977.

Dear Stephen,

How strange! what you hurl at me as an insult I receive as a compliment: "you are a traditionalist at heart".

Yes, indeed. Everything I am and have has been handed on to me in one way or another. In the first place it all flows from God but, with infinite delicacy, He bestows His bounty through other hands. God seems a little diffident at appearing to buy our love—but He need not worry: we are too proud to show Him gratitude. Anyway, it is from other hands that we receive His bounty. My life itself was handed on to me by my parents. And with what toil and self-sacrifice they preserved it! It was from my father that I received my notion of discipline and rectitude, mixed with the necessary tinge of "under-statementship" to make me truly English. My religion was given to me from the penny catechism at my mother's knee: I have none other. What a horrid boy I was, in whom conceit and laziness vied for the mastery: yet my teachers managed to transmit to me the basis of whatever culture I possess. Later, at the seminary, those dear professors gave me all they knew of the doctrines and traditions of the One True Church. Then I was ordained priest with the "tradition of the instruments" for the Divine Sacrifice and by the laying-on of hands.

Even what is most intimate: my spirituality, my prayer— which is known to none but God and me, which turns an objective truth into a living reality—yes, even this has been handed on to me by Augustine, Gertrude, Suso, Sales, Teresa and a host of others.

It is absolutely untrue to say that I am a bundle of sensations. In the first place I am a bundle of traditions. It is by my traditions that I judge the sensations of experience. Without them no sensation would have significance. The traditions form the warp and experience the woof of that wonder-

28

ful tapestry which we call the human person. If an experience can be absorbed by my traditions, then it is woven into the tissue of my personality. If not, it is rejected. I doubt if the warp, the tradition is ever rejected: it is loosened or pulled tighter to catch the woof of experience. If it still fails, then there is a hole in the personality—people we call "chipped." Yes, Stephen, you are as much a traditionalist as I. And if you start denying your traditions you know the outcome: you will become bitter, cruel—chipped.

They are all dead now, the people who have formed me, from whose hands I have received God's bounty. Alas, alas! little gratitude did I show them while they lived. I give it now, too late. I sometimes wince with pain, not from shame at past ingratitude, but from the joy of present thankfulness. Jeer at me if you will but it is true. Small wonder, then, that I should refuse new gifts, be they from the Pope in person, if it means rejecting the gifts I have accepted from those who made me. One is free to refuse a gift: it is dishonourable to return one.

In our days it is fashionable to say that "the Church's Tradition must not be confused with the traditions in the Church." Like all contemporary clichés it is ambiguous. Its promoters, I suspect, mean that there is no other revelation than the Church itself, the Kingdom; and all the rest is relative and subject to change. But I imagine that you use it to mean that Revealed Truth is one thing whereas its traditional expression and the reaction of the faithful are quite another. Well, they cannot be separated—at least not just like that. A thing can only be revealed if it is expressed: the expression is the revelation. As for the reaction of the faithful, I know nothing more beautiful in all God's exuberant creation than their piety, more humble than the violet, grander than the Himalayas. I love the crucifix worn flat by generations of lips; I love the *Garden of the Soul* with the binding bursting from countless mortuary-cards; I love the rosary polished by fingering; I love the artificial flowers around the oleograph of Our Lady; I love the hideous water-stoop held by a Guardian Angel which adorns the bedroom. It is all beautiful because it is pathetic; what the revolutionaries do is all ugly because it is presumptuous.

Incidentally, I rather wonder how far Pope, bishop and priest have a right to interfere with the piety of the faithful.

Canon Law has nothing to say on the subject; prudence has something; justice a lot. In this connection it should be remembered that the expressions of revelation—particularly the Mass—are not only dogmatic formulas but also objects of devotion.

Anyway, how can one prevent the faithful from reacting to revelation? It is quite simple: by making them doubt what God has revealed. Nevertheless, in the present revolution salvation can only come from the traditional piety of the faithful.

I suppose, in the last resort, it is his moral attitude rather than his intellectual ferment which I hold against the revolutionary. Does he really believe that he is a "self-made man?" Has he no humility, no piety, no gratitude? Is he quite certain that the living laity are all fools and that he descends from an inexplicable succession of infants? He has the effrontery to call himself an "adult Christian," in spite of the fact that, almost seventy-eight years ago today, Leo XIII (in his Apostolic Letter to Cardinal Gibbons of Baltimore of January 24th, 1899) condemned absolutely the opinion that "the Church should be more adaptable to the civilization of a world which has arrived at manhood"—which at last is adult. Adult Christians must be pretty senile by now.

That is enough, I could go on forever. I have written you a sort of confession and I hope that you will give me absolution, although I have no intention whatsoever to amend my ways.

◇　◇　◇

6.　To Henry Dobson, Bishop of Hunstanton.
Wednesday, January 19th, 1977.

Dear Harry,

I have so far read an odd half-dozen letters from the brethren, all kind and sympathetic (except one), although all critical (except one)—which I well understand. What does surprise me, however, is that none of you attack what I actually say in my little Bomb. You all attack my general attitude and from refreshingly different angles: I cannot send you a duplicated reply. One implies that I follow my heart rather than my head; another that I am divisive; a third that I am not forward-looking or again, but slightly differently, that I am a mere traditionalist, etc. . . . All of which is true in its way but I fail to see how it invalidates the simple, practical solution set out in my Bomb. You are no exception. In fact you say so: I am wrong "not on account of the merit or otherwise of your action nor because of its possible illegality but because it is clearly against the trend of history." Dear me! one can scarcely be more "general" than that.

I wonder what you mean. Perhaps you were only thinking of the immediate future: Rome, my fellow bishops, many of the clergy and a few of the laity will combine to make my life so intolerable that I shall be obliged to cave in. This is indeed possible but is scarcely history. No, you mean History with a capital H, which has nothing to do with the past, little with the present but has a lot to say about the future. You do not accept the Christian conception of history, so wonderfully formulated by Augustine, Bossuet and de Maistre, or you would be diffident in dubbing me "untrendy." Quite rightly, you do not accept the "pendulum" idea (which is not even an accurate description apart from not explaining the mechanism of the clock), since you think of History as a one-way street, a trend. Perhaps you have in mind the Apocalyptic view, so optimistic in Marx and Teilhard but tinged with pessimism in Hegel and Schopenhauer? No, I doubt it, knowing you as I do. I think it more likely that you have simply returned to the "Fates" of pagan mythology, against whose decrees even the nod of Zeus was inoperative—or, to be more accurate, as soon as they started spinning Zeus nodded off to sleep. Anyway, whatever your view of History, my action is against the trend because it is not "revolting" enough, in both senses of the term.

Now, I have my own private view of History. I accept that a struggle it is—even a constant state of revolution. It started straight away in the Garden of Eden. I also admit that the revolution always succeeds. But what is so puzzling is that the moment it succeeds it is obliged to start all over again from scratch. It always triumphs but never conquers. The USSR today is a living example of what I mean. After sixty years of straining away at the most ruthless and continuous revolution in history it is no further advanced than in October 1917. It has massacred untold millions of people, all of whom appear to have resurrected again. In fact it has taken sixty years for it to beget its most astonishing and least

31

desired product, Alexander Solzhenitsyn. You see the point? Strange, isn't it?

This seems to me to be the process. Neat, logical little men, preferably lawyers, are forever attempting to reduce God's magnificent, incomprehensible, chaotic creation to the neatness and logic of their own beastly little minds. Of course they succeed in a way, rationalizing everything around them until it stops working altogether. They can rationalize the egg industry so as to guarantee equality of egglessness for all but they cannot pass a law requiring all hens to lay another egg. If they do—and it happens—the hens are unlikely to play ball or, in the present case, eggs. The trouble is that God's creation cannot be reduced to rational order. It is bigger than logic; if it is rationalized at one point, it will pop up at another. Hence the endless and heroic fight of the revolutionary. I suppose that Robespierre will forever remain the ideal type: such a nice little lawyer, as neat and tidy in his mind as in his pale blue frock-coat, and so full of "virtue" and so "incorruptible" that only he could organize the Terror.

Anyway, my point is that the revolutionary process is the eternal attempt of man to impose his order, his law on God's creation. And this is exactly what is happening in the Church. Until this post-conciliar period, God's Church appeared almost as magnificent, incomprehensible and chaotic as His creation. It was cluttered up indiscriminately with tiaras, cardinals' hats, mitres, birettas of every hue and shape, rosaries, prie-dieus, saints and sinners, Friday fish, indulgences, blessings, statues, pilgrimages, tonsured monks and nuns with variously goffered coiffes, processions, confessionals, banners, plain-chant, unplain-chant and all the rest. Yes, cluttered up it was—as is the universe. But it all worked incredibly smoothly. The most absurdly shaped pieces fitted into their allotted places in the puzzle. And the overall picture which the puzzle produced was one of extraordinary unity—again just like the creation.

After Vatican II the neat, logical little fellows were given their head. Obviously, the first thing to do was to clear the decks. A clean sweep has been made of absolutely everything. Not only was the Tiara flogged but even the Pietà got chipped. Then they must produce a neat, logical little liturgy: unpretentious, comprehensible, as dull as themselves. The laity promptly participated by walking out. That is the process all along the line.

Now, am I acting as you say "clean against the trend of history?" Yes, if you regard the revolutionary process as the constitutive element of history. No, if you think of me as the dull, elemental matter of God's creation popping up inevitably from the very nature of things. That I personally shall be ground to dust is not unlikely; but the reality I stand for will still pop up when the neat, logical little men find themselves holding a handful of dust.

Quite logically, you accuse me of fighting for a lost cause. My dear Harry, it is among the greatest compliments you can pay me. Perhaps my only inveterate sin is my contempt (alas!) for those who jump on bandwagons. Surely lost causes are the only ones worth fighting for? Why don battle dress for a victory parade? And surely you do not believe that what is lost by men is lost to God?

A thousand apologies for being such a bore—but it is in part your fault for writing so interesting a letter.

◇   ◇   ◇

7.   To George Weir, Archbishop of Derby.
Thursday, January 20th, 1977.

Dear George,

Your letter caused me no surprise. You pride yourself on being the rudest member of the hierarchy. It is a claim in which you rarely fail. You accuse me of holding the New Ordo to be invalid—which I don't; of undermining the authority of the episcopate—which I am trying to restore; of being disloyal to Pope, Council, you, my colleagues, and all and sundry—which needs examining; of using the Mass as a banner for revolt—which is nonsense, etc. . . . It is a fairly formidable indictment, isn't it, even for you?

However, I am interested in your accusation of disloyalty. I know exactly what you mean but I happen to see things exactly in reverse. The trouble is that people always think of loyalty as being due to themselves. You automatically think of loyalty working upwards. This is natural as you spring from a well-to-do family, employers in business and with staff in your home. I, on the other hand, come from an eminently respectable but very poor background—hewers of wood in Roding Forest. I, consequently, think of loyalty as working downwards. I don't say that the Squire wasn't tough—he

33

was—but we knew he would see us through: he was loyal to us humble folk. Incidentally, it was he, not the diocese, who paid for my seminary—although he was a Black Protestant and always called us "my bloody Papists with too many blasted brats." As for Her Ladyship, she was a deal sight better than Social Security—but I must not bore you with reminiscences. You see the point? You blame me for not being loyal to my superiors. It has never crossed my mind: they are perfectly capable of defending themselves and even of breaking me if they so wish—which they doubtless will if I appear to succeed. I, on the other hand, accuse you of being disloyal to your inferiors, your flock. It has never crossed your mind, although they are totally defenceless against you. And your disloyalty, George, is quite irreparable: thanks to it countless souls are seared in this life and may be lost in the next. My disloyalty to you can do little more than melt your collar—if, in fact, I am disloyal.

Disloyalty to the Pope is a more serious accusation. Although I have been a bishop for practically twelve years, I have only seen him thrice and then in a gaggle with other bishops. He did not impress me as being a particularly congenial type: intelligent enough, but weak and consequently devious. He knows his own mind all right, but he struck me as the sort of fellow who would get his way by hook or crook because he is incapable of getting it straight. But that is scarcely the point, is it? We are not talking about the Pope as a person but about the divine institution of the Papacy. It is abundantly clear that loyalty to the divine institution is quite distinct from loyalty to its temporary incumbent. Indeed, the two can run clean contrary to each other as history illustrates on almost every page from St Paul onwards. My favorite example is the Blessed Colomba of Rieti. You certainly do not know the story since your reading is confined to watching television. (You see, I can be as rude as you if I like.)

Anyway, Colomba was a Dominican nun who lived in Perugia. She suffered from almost every type of mystical phenomenon—ecstasy, inedia, levitation and the rest. The Master of the Dominicans felt uncertain whether her spirit was from God or from the Devil. This was about 1490, when people still believed in both. In consequence he would have the girl examined by the Holy Father himself who was on a visit to his favourite son, Cesare. This was duly arranged. In the great hall at Perugia, which you have doubtless visited, there sat enthroned the Sovereign Pontiff, Alexander VI, with Cesare on his right, Lucrezia on his left and the Papal Court around. Colomba was introduced. Upon sight of the Vicar of Christ she immediately went into ecstasy, as should all good nuns. I seem to remember that she levitated and railed at the Pope from somewhere near the ceiling. "You who are the Vicar of Christ and act as the vicar of Satan! You who hold the Keys of the Kingdom but only unlock the doors of brothels! You who are captain of the Ark of Salvation and have a girl in every port! You who. . . ." After twenty minutes of this sort of stuff, the Papal Court felt rather anxious for poor Colomba's safety. How do you get girls out of ecstasy? However, Alexander Borgia turned to the Master of the Dominicans: "Have no fear, my son; her spirit is certainly from God since everything she says is true."

I sometimes wish that I were an ecstatic Dominican nun. I could keep going for well over twenty minutes. What I doubt is whether the sixth Paul has the humility of the sixth Alexander. Admittedly, it is far more difficult to be humble if one sins between the ears than if one sins between the sheets. Anyway, the point is perfectly clear: Colomba was in opposition to the person of the Pope precisely out of loyalty to the institution of the Papacy.

What I find astonishing in our days is that the situation is exactly reversed. People can attack the Papacy to their heart's content provided they do not breathe a word against the person of the Pope. Our own ecumenists see the Pope as a Constitutional Monarch with plenty of whiskers but no teeth. Hans Küng is even against the whiskers. Dom Bernard Bresnet thinks that the Papacy should be a committee with, possibly, a lady chairman. Professor Delumeau would prefer the pope to be the quinquennially elected President of the World Council of Churches. All these—and I could name others—are in keeping with the present regime, and Delumeau can even expect a lollypop in his stocking at Christmas. On the other hand, that benign old gentleman, Archbishop Lefebvre, gets into endless trouble for maintaining that the personal administration of the present Pontiff is an unmitigated disaster.

Enough of all that. What I am getting at is perfectly clear. You should think twice before you start talking about loyalty.

It is certainly you who are disloyal downwards. It is also possible that you are disloyal upwards to the divine institution of the Papacy precisely by toadying to its temporary administrator.

I could fill another couple of pages on your accusation that I use the Mass as a banner of revolt. The trouble is that you have the mind of a drill sergeant. You could not care less in which direction the platoon is marching provided it keeps in step. When, at the edge of a precipice, the troops break formation and scurry off, you accuse them of indiscipline.

Excuse me if I appear to answer you with a bit of your own coinage, but it does not prevent me from being

Ever devotedly in Dmno,

◇　◇　◇

LETTERS TO DIOCESAN CLERGY

The Catholic Directory supplies the following statistics for the diocese of Stamford:

```
Diocesan clergy working in the diocese  . . . . . . . . . . 145
Priests of Religious Orders, Congregations and
                      Societies  . . . . . . . . . . . . . . . . . 92
                                                        237
Convents of Religious Women  . . . . . . . . . . . . . . . . . . . 34
```

The "estimated Catholic population" is given as 80,000 although it is obvious from the Baptismal Registers that there are at least twice that number.

◇　◇　◇

I have no means of knowing the number of diocesan clergy who called personally on their bishop during the first week. Neither do I know their reaction to the Ad clerum. *Twenty-three seem to have written to him—at least there are twenty-three replies. Of these, twelve were in enthusiastic support of their bishop's solution; eight appear to have been favourable but had diverse difficul-*

ties, problems or queries of varying importance; three were in absolute opposition.

The twelve in support of Bishop Forester received very much the same replies. Doubtless the Bishop made a draft to which Canon Cocksedge and Father FitzHenry added the details. Here is a typical example.

8.   To the Parish Priest of a medium-sized Parish.
Tuesday, January 18th, 1977.

I cannot sufficiently express my gratitude for your support. Without a determinate number (say 25%) of the parochial clergy solidly behind me, it would be impossible for me to implement my intentions. I should have to resign, leaving loyal Catholics in a far worse condition than they are now, with hopes deceived and in consequent despair. Without your support, my legacy to the diocese would have been nothing but confusion, bitterness and frustration. And please thank Fathers X & Y (the curate and convent chaplain) with all the sincerity of which I am capable. Three priests in a fairly nodal parish such as yours is indeed heartening news.

I can well believe the enthusiasm of your flock, although in some measure it probably reflected yours—for which all honour to you. The revolution set the clergy against the laity: what an experience it is to be united again! I witnessed it here at the Cathedral. I was in the porch after all Masses except the 11 o'clock which I celebrated. It was unbelievable. People kissed my hands, my pectoral Cross, the hem of my cassock, anything they could get hold of; they rubbed me with their rosaries as though I were a relic. "It's wonderful to feel a Catholic again" was the predominant remark and they twittered like little birds in the car park, casting sly looks back at me to make sure that I was real. I could have cried; in fact I did.

The high Mass at 11 was quite extraordinary. Doubtless word had got round the town, the suburbs and even some of the villages. The Cathedral was packed as I have never seen it, right out into the car park. I read and explained the *Ad clerum*. I finished. There was a moment of intense silence. Then somebody yelled "God bless you!" Then everybody started cheering, yelling, clapping. It was only drowned when the organ pulled out all the stops for Credo III. The vast volume of noise suddenly merged into the Act of Faith. How beautiful—and how pathetic. Yes, Father, we must not allow their hopes to be dashed.

The trouble is that enthusiasm is a flame. It has got to be canalized so as to warm the heart and keep it beating to the rhythm of the Sacred Heart. I wonder how that can be done? Clearly music can help: the simple plain-chant Masses would knock out all those ridiculous hymns. They would have to be taught in school, of course. Perhaps the Guild of the Blessed Sacrament ought to be revived and attached in some way to the Immemorial Mass; also solemn Benediction, with the priest as chaplain rather than as president. Incidentally, how I hate that word "President," as though I were elected by men instead of being called by God. No, I am an artisan, a member of the priest-craft, who lays on the Divine Presence as the plumber lays on water. Anyway, this wonderful enthusiasm will have to be institutionalized or it will burn out. You know your parishioners much better than do I: I should be most grateful for your advice.

I do wish to warn you, however, that plenty of opposition will rear its ugly head. My *Ad clerum* has taken the revolutionaries completely by surprise but they will immediately react and quickly get organized. You will certainly receive anonymous letters. You may have to face an active core of resistance in your parish. The Catholic press is bound to be as unfavourably disposed towards my action as yesterday's secular press was favourably inclined. It will certainly help you to face the opposition if you form a close confraternity of likeminded priests who meet regularly once a week.

Again, I thank you for your support. I never doubted it but am not less grateful to have it.

◇   ◇   ◇

Of the eight priests who had problems, difficulties or queries, four were dismissed kindly but fairly peremptorily. At least Bishop Forester's answers do not seem to me to be of general interest. Two raised the same problem of concelebration. They were answered very similarly and I publish a relevant extract in letter 9 below. The two others received substantial replies.

9.   Extract from letters to two Parish Priests on the subject of concelebration. Both letters are dated Tuesday, January 18th, 1977.

I am vaguely surprised that you should feel so strongly in favour of concelebration because I happen to hate it myself. After all, we concelebrate with Jesus. To have Tom, Dick and Harry concelebrating as well does not add to the intimacy with the Divine Co-Celebrant. It may not detract but can certainly distract from that intimacy. You obviously feel otherwise since you talk of the sense of comradeship in Christ which you feel at concelebrations. Mind you, comradeship in Christ is not the same as comradeship with Christ.

However, to come to your specific question: Yes. The Immemorial Rite and my hybrid are not intended for concelebration and are in fact unsuitable since they are silent. Concelebrants should consequently use the New Ordo plus, of course, the Offertory prayers from the Tridentine missal. Such, at least, is my present view.

I am grateful to you for bringing up this matter as I should probably never have thought of it myself. Moreover, I am so prejudiced against concelebration that I doubt my ability to give a fair ruling on it. Your letter has the merit of reminding me that others think otherwise. In view of all which, I shall submit the whole question to the Chapter when it meets on Thursday. I shall ask it to make a careful study of concelebration under every aspect and submit to me its recommendations in due course. This may take six months or more, so, in the meantime, please follow my recommendation above: New Ordo plus old Offertory. I shall hand your letter to the Provost but perhaps you would care to write to him directly.

You may well ask why I should be so anti-concelebration. I have already given you the fundamental reason: we are co-celebrant with Jesus and a thousand human co-celebrants still only make one Mass. To put it very mildly, the multiplication of human co-celebrants makes it appear as though the efficacy of Mass was dependent on the presence and intention of priests rather than on the presence and will of Christ. For two priests to concelebrate one Mass is not the same as for them to celebrate two Masses.

But I have other reasons as well—notably the abuses to which concelebration is prone. You remember the requiem for poor Father Roy Burns last June? Unfortunately I was unable to be present; had I been, I should have stopped the whole proceedings. Perhaps you were one of the co-celebrants? Fortunately I do not know. However, the last straw occurred in July. Admittedly it was in France but we need not imagine that such things do not happen here.

I was staying with a priest friend in the South of France. We did not concelebrate: I said Mass first, then he. Incidentally, we used the Immemorial Rite. On the second day my friend was reading the Gospel when a couple of scruffy individuals plonked themselves down in the pews. Having finished the Gospel, my friend turned to them and asked if they wished to receive Holy Communion—in order to consecrate the small hosts as, of course, there was no reservation in the church. They did. When Mass was over they followed us into the sacristy. One of them said to my friend: "Mon Dieu! That was difficult; we have both forgotten the old Mass—but we probably got the words of consecration near enough." I was horrified. "So you are both priests," I asked, "and you concelebrated that Mass?" "Yes." "And did you take a stipend for it?" "Of course. Pourquoi pas?"

Am I being fussy? Certainly there was no great sense of comradeship in Christ at such a concelebration. But even at the best of times, surely it is monstrous for every priest to take a stipend for one and the same Mass? Please send your comments to the Provost.

◇ ◇ ◇

10. To the Parish Priest of a large parish with four curates. Wednesday, January 19th, 1977.

Dear——

A thousand congratulations! Fancy getting that mob to agree as to what they are going to do. I roared with merriment at your description of the little cock-sparrow who scarcely remembers the old rite in Latin, has not a clue how to say it and knows no Latin anyway but now insists on saying none other! Typical somehow. But, as far as I am concerned, bravo! for the little cock-sparrow.

40

I am not as surprised as you about your guru.* I think he invented queer ceremonies of his own because, basically, he found the New Ordo inadequate. If you remember, I attended one at your request. I was rather impressed although it is not the sort of thing I should do myself. The fact is that the old rite is patient of mystical interpretation whereas the new is not. One cannot even "pray" the new rite—and indeed one is not meant to. It is what it claims to be: a jolly community gathering ending in a symbolic bun-fight. I doubt if your particular guru will be the only one to stop innovating as soon as he is allowed to say the real thing.

Your other two men are perfectly reasonable fellows. Unfortunately, you will be losing one in the near future: it is time he got a parish. Heaven alone knows whom I shall be able to send you.

Anyway, that all seems splendid. I have not made your life intolerable. You know, that was one of the things I feared most: that in big parishes such as yours my Bomb might increase the strain between the clergy: It does not seem to have done so in yours, thank God! That is doubtless due to your judicious handling. Incidentally, I am glad that you approve of my hybrid solution.

You ask me, however, a question which I find almost impossible to answer: "If you thought that one day you would have to draw the line, why on earth did you wait until everybody had got used to the new dispensation?"

What a difficult question! I shall take the last phrase first: "everybody has got used to the new dispensation." Have they? I am not sure. Myself, I should have said "resigned" rather than "used." However, if your flock really is used to it, this can only be because (to your eternal honour) you have been using the new dispensation improperly: everything is done with the decorum and piety of the old dispensation. The whole point of the new line is that it implies perpetual change. That people should "get used to it" is what most it dreads. If they do, then it is high time to do something else. Of its nature, the new religion is dynamic; what one gets used to is automatically static. All your people were perfectly used

---

* *(Editor's note: a middle-aged curate with a "spiritual family" and interested in mysticism.)*

41

to the old rite; that is exactly what was wrong with it, the ONLY thing wrong with it to the progressive eye. In your parish, the new look is now no different from the old: it is "what people are used to"; it should, therefore, immediately be changed. What has happened is that a philosophy of "becoming" has replaced the philosophy of "being." The trouble with it is that: if everything must change, then it is not worth changing anything. Exactly—and that is why I propose to return to the changeless. Have I made myself clear?

Now to the first part of your question: "If you thought that one day you would have to draw the line, why did you wait?" Ah! my dear, who knows? Cowardice? Hypocrisy? Ambition? Because I was used to obeying? Stupidity? Human respect? You can accuse me to your heart's content and I shall not deny you. I do not know; God knows. I can, however, rationalize my delay in drawing the line although, pray God, I shall never have the impudence to justify it. I saw what was happening away back in the 1950s, when I succeeded my friend, Bryan Houghton, as secretary of the Higher Studies Conference. The ends to which the Council were put caused me no surprise. But I knew that those serried ranks of mitred gentlemen were not crooks; they had been knocked off balance but would soon regain it. I accepted to become a bishop in 1965 because I was asked to do something which I knew I could: keep accounts. In 1969 the New Ordo was promulgated. This is when I should have drawn the line. My friend did and with the maximum publicity: his was the test case. He is basically a simple soul. He thought that all priests loved their Mass far more than did he. It only required an example. If a clown like himself could stand up for the Mass, then all the holy Joes would be up in arms. As you know, not one was—not even you or I. I hesitated. Timing seemed important. I consulted Heenan. He got the Indult in the following year. Hope (as I thought) germinated in my heart. It was not hope at all but plain, stupid optimism. But now, by 1977, my optimism has withered and the climate has changed. Concerning my optimism, the less said the better. Concerning the climate, you are in as good a position as I to judge. Even one year ago, could you, for all your dexterity, have got your curates to react as they have now? And you, how would you have reacted one year ago?

Have I answered your question? But please do not imagine that cowardice, servile obedience, indolence, stupidity, hypocrisy, ambition, human respect and the rest would not supply you with just as good an answer.

Pray for me,

◇　◇　◇

11.　To the Reverend Giles Pocock, Parish Priest of Blackwater

(Blackwater is a "plum" parish with no curates and no schools; just two Masses on Sundays. He was formerly Professor of Fundamental Theology at a major seminary.)

Thursday, January 20th, 1977.

Dear Father Pocock,

I was most grateful to receive your letter because it put my mind at rest. I am terrified of you theologians. You seem to have gone charismatic and to "speak with tongues" which we common mortals fail to understand—although I sometimes suspect that you merely have your tongue in your cheek.

It is very good of you to consent to put the prayers of the old Offertory back in their place in spite of your reservations about their significance. I am delighted, too, that you should approve by and large of my "hybrid." So your 9 a.m. will be the New Ordo plus the Offertory and the 11 o'clock the "hybrid." Yes, that is perfectly all right by me. I vaguely hope, however, that from time to time you will give your parishioners the Immemorial Rite should they ask for it. Surely you have a hard core of Tridentiners who are led by the Duchess? Perhaps that is the trouble: you feel it would be unwise to allow the Duchess' clique to triumph too openly, too easily and too soon.

You give me, however, a quite different reason which both interests me and which I completely fail to understand. You say that on balance you disapprove of the old rite and approve of the new because it is your function "to mediate religion to your people." Doubtless you have to mediate it to them in catechism classes, sermons, conferences and the like, but surely not at Mass? What you do at Mass is exactly the reverse: You "mediate the religion of the people to the Heav-

43

enly Father through Jesus Christ truly present on the altar."

You seem to me to have defined with wonderful clarity the basic difference between the new rite and the old. If you think of Mass as "mediating religion to the people" then clearly it should be comprehensible, i.e. in the vernacular, and didactic, i.e. with lots of scripture readings and homilies; moreover, the people should demonstrate that they have received the message by constant "participation" at every level and in diverse forms—exclamations, hymns, gestures. If, on the other hand, you think of Mass as "mediating the religion of the people to God," then, as a matter of fact, there is nothing for it but silence.

What do I, Edmund Forester, imagine is happening during Mass in the old rite? Quite simple. After a bit of back-chat, Epistles and Gospels and things, I uncover the instruments of my craft and lay on the sacrifice of Man's Redemption in much the same way as a plumber lays on water. Yes, but the people? They start subsiding. Some meditate for a moment but soon give up; some thumb a prayer book without much conviction; some finger a rosary without thinking; the majority just sit or kneel and become empty. They have their distractions, of course, but as far as they are able they are recollected. You see, the state of prayer of the overwhelming majority of the faithful is that of "simple regard."

Good, they are now recollected. Human activity is reduced to its minimum. Then the miracle occurs. At the fine apex of their souls, imperceptible even to themselves, the Holy Ghost starts making little shrieks of "Abba, Father" or, after the consecration, soft groans of the Holy Name, "Jesu, Jesu." They adore: or rather, to be more accurate, the Holy Ghost adores within them. Sometimes, as I stand at the altar, I can feel the myriad little darts of adoration piercing my back and landing on the Adorable Presence. That is what I mean by "mediating the religion of the people of God."

"Nonsense, Forester," I can hear you say, "you are being sentimental." No I am not; it is merely that I am fairly sensitive. How often have I been almost deafened by the piety of the faithful, now, alas, struck dumb by sing-songs!

I ought to write a thousand boring letters but I must tell you a story. I had been Parish Priest of Grumby for a couple of years. In a remote village lived a certain Mrs Donkin, mother of five children under ten, of whom the last was born after her husband was killed in an accident. They had to walk a couple of miles to catch the bus, which did not correspond at all conveniently with Masses. The mother and elder children carried the baby in turn; the toddlers toddled. Never did they miss Mass except when there was snow. Because of the bus, they arrived rather early for the 9:30 and plonked themselves down in their pew, with a potty for the toddlers, carefully camouflaged in a scarlet bandanna. There they sat. They never moved. Mrs Donkin neither stood for the Gospel nor knelt at the Sanctus. The only kneeling was when Mrs Donkin and the eldest boy were at the Communion rail.

I used to call on them about once a quarter. I was still young and had the illusion that I could "do good." The second child was going to make her first Holy Communion and I thought it would be a good excuse to give Mrs D. a really decent missal and appropriate prayer books for the rest. To introduce the subject I said to Mrs D.: "I notice that at Mass you don't use a rosary or missal or anything. What do you do, Mrs Donkin?" Without a moment's thought or hesitation the answer came: "I sits there and I loves." When anyone starts criticizing the piety of the laity, the harsh voice of Mrs Donkin rings in my ears: "I sits there and I loves." St Teresa of Avila could say no more.

No, Father, I do not mediate religion to Mrs Donkin. By the grace of ordination I mediate her religion to the One she loves.

Forgive me, Father, but in my present troubles it is a relief to write about the only thing that matters: the adoration of God.

Devotedly in Dmno,

◇　◇　◇

Of the three diocesan priests who were in direct opposition to Bishop Forester, I have no scruple in mentioning the name of Father Roderic Sludge. His case became notorious thanks to a certain section of the press. Even the popular Catholic papers took up his cause until it was realized that, far from damaging the bishop's reputation, it rallied the uncommitted to his side. The laity felt that here at last was a bishop who was willing to defend their religion.

I am in possession of a substantial dossier concerning Father Sludge. In order to make the bishop's letter com-

prehensible I shall quote from the report made by Sludge's dean, the Very Reverend Nial McCarthy, and dated December 13th, 1976.

Father Sludge is a reasonably young man of 43. He was appointed chaplain to the Veronican Convent at Horethorpe Hall because he had suffered an operation for peritonitis which had left him rather weak. The medical profession advised against the irregular hours and meals which are a common feature of the normal presbytery.

Horethorpe Hall is a fine neo-classic mansion built in 1810 and standing in about eighty acres of park land. There is also a large dower-house, The Court, on the property. It was bought in 1923 by the Sisters of St Veronica, who ran a highly successful girls' boarding school in it until this was closed in the summer of 1973. Most of the nuns were sent to other houses of the Congregation. The eight who remained ran a centre for ecumenical and progressive gatherings of one sort or another. The chapel was the former ballroom, a splendid room about eighty foot long and twenty wide with an orchestra gallery at one end.

12.   The Report of the Very Reverend Nial McCarthy.

My Lord,

I shall endeavour to make this report as factual as I can without introducing personal comments.

On Sunday, December 12th, 1976, I arrived at the Convent of St Veronica at Horethorpe Hall at 9:40 a.m. upon instructions from Your Lordship to assist at the Eucharistic celebration which was due to start at 10 a.m. The front door was closed. I rang the bell. The door was opened by a sister whom I recognized. She was dressed in a white pullover and white slacks, skin-tight around the hips and thighs. I explained: "I have come to assist at your Mass on instructions from the Bishop." "I'll just get Fr Sludge." He appeared. He was dressed in a curious sort of cassock, oddly cut and in a shiny black material, rather like very thin patent leather. I repeated that I had come to assist at Mass upon Your Lordship's instruction. "Splendid! Why not concelebrate?" he asked. "I've got a cassock that will fit you. You see, we are very old-fashioned here and still wear them." I replied that

I had not come to concelebrate but to watch. "That's a pity: our Mass needs participation to be properly understood. However, if you won't I suppose you'd better go up into the gallery." I was duly conducted thither. The nuns used to use it as a choir loft. The little organ was still there as were shelves filled with the *Liber Usualis* and other chant books. It was clear that it had not been used for a long time.

From the gallery I had a good view of the chapel except, of course, for the entrance which was directly below me. There was no sign of the Holy Faith whatsoever: no crucifix, no picture of Our Lady, no kneelers, not even any pews. The central portion, apart from some chairs against walls, was completely empty. At the far end but standing well away from the wall was a fair sized table, about eight foot by four, in the centre of which was a large earthenware bowl capable of holding four pints or more. To the left of the bowl was a bread-board and knife with a long loaf, not unlike a French baguette but a little thicker. To the right stood six litre bottles of white wine with removable capsules.

I could not see the congregation arriving because, as I have said, the entrance was below the gallery. They turned up quite punctually at 10 a.m. and I could hear a lot of friendly greeting and chatter as well as the clatter of cup and cutlery. I presume that refreshments were served before Mass.

At 10:10 a.m. they all moved into the centre of the ball-room where I could plainly see them. There were nine men including Fr Sludge and fourteen women of whom six were nuns. There should be eight nuns at the convent; I do not know where the missing two were. All the men were wearing the same curious cassock as Fr Sludge, whose only distin-guishing mark was a black scarf or stole. The women were all dressed like the nun who had opened the door to me, in white pull-overs and slacks. I presume that this uniform has some significance which is unknown to me.

Of the eight men other than Fr Sludge I only recognized two: one runs a successful ladies' outfitters in Horebury and is reputedly a homosexual; the other is an unsuccessful den-tist. Of the women, I recognized four apart from the nuns: the dentist's wife and a youngish widow of about 40 who has come down in the world; also two ex-convent girls, one of whom was involved in a drug case.

They stood in front of the chairs, facing each other across the ballroom. A hymn was sung which I did not recognize. Fr Sludge made an extempore prayer concerning "welcome in love." The chairs were then drawn into a circle and Fr Sludge asked if anyone had read anything of interest during the week. Five answered up, two men and three women. I got the impression that this was pre-arranged, not spontaneous. Short passages were read and followed by a shorter commentary. Three of the passages came from reviews and had nothing to do with religion; one, read by a nun, was a highly salacious extract from Aubrey Beardsley; one was culled from Karl Marx. Father Sludge alone read from the Bible: it was the story of Rahab from Josue 2. His commentary was: "The People of God can only expect salvation from those who have plumbed the depths of their own incarnation—our presence in flesh and blood—like Rahab the prostitute." There followed three minutes of silent meditation at the end of which Father Sludge, still sitting, made another extempore prayer concerning "Unity in love and love in unity, especially under persecution."

I must say that all the above was done very expertly and smoothly, as though much practiced. It had scarcely taken twenty minutes. It was not quite 10:30 a.m.

All rose and the chairs were replaced against the wall. A young man produced a large metal gong and two young women steel-strung guitars of the Hawaiian variety. Another hymn was sung, about the spirit of God vivifying matter. The hymn stopped but the guitars and gong continued. The congregation joined hands and started to whine rather like the guitars. The noise increased until it became quite deafening. The instrumentalists, who were inaudible by now, joined the circle. After three minutes of the deafening whine, the dentist suddenly gave a great shriek, broke the circle and came into the middle. His eyes were wide open but staring as though they saw nothing. He started yelling gibberish at the top of his voice. The rest of the congregation subsided into a low, monotonous whine, except for a young man who occasionally barked like a dog. Father Sludge was standing quite motionless, eyes and lips shut; I doubt if he joined in the whining. After the dentist had been shrieking for nearly a minute, he was joined by a nun and then by three more members of the congregation. They performed slightly differently, some being more articulate than others. I could distinguish words such as Yahveh, Jesu, Adonai, Kyrie and a few English ones such as Spirit, God, love and the like. It did not last very long. From the dentist's first shriek to the gradual subsidence in mutterings there were only eight minutes.

As the glossolalists came to a halt, the rest of the congregation stopped whining, broke the circle and started hugging and kissing first the glossolalist and then each other. They appeared to be in a trance, as though sleepwalking. Father Sludge did as they, but was obviously in full possession of his faculties; the difference between him and rest was most marked, albeit impossible to describe. As they hugged and kissed they uttered such exclamations as: "the Spirit has spoken," "we have heard the Spirit," "let us keep the Spirit in our minds and bodies"—but I doubt if they knew what they were saying. This lasted quite an appreciable time, about twelve minutes.

At a sign from Father Sludge the gong player took his instrument into the far right hand corner of the room, the other side of the table. He then said to the congregation: "Having shown our love to our neighbour, let us now show our love for Jesus." He then led them, holding hands, round the table at the other end of the room until they again formed a circle. The gong had started up again, at first distantly. It grew louder and more rhythmical. The circle was set in motion around the table but fairly slowly, as in a tango. The congregation was just starting to make inarticulate noises when a woman's voice carried out: "When two or three are gathered together in your name, Jesus, you are present." This was the sign for the gong to beat faster and faster, louder and louder. The congregation then began shouting repeatedly and quite indiscriminately: "This is my body; this is my blood— my body, my blood": on and on. People broke away from the circle to cut themselves a slice of bread and drink deeply from the bowl, which was refilled from the bottles. I could not make out whether Father Sludge said the words himself.

My Lord, I felt sick. I was overcome by a terrible sensation of sadness bordering on despair. I feared for my sanity. It took all the courage and energy I possess to get up and get out. I left at 11:06.

I am sorry, my Lord, I do not know how the ceremony ended.

The above is a true statement of what I saw and heard

49

at the Convent of St Veronica at Horethorpe Hall on Sunday, December 12th, 1976.

In faith of which etc. . . .

Nial McCarthy
Dean.

◇   ◇   ◇

13.   To the Reverend Roderic Sludge at Horethorpe Hall. Thursday, January 20th, 1977.

Father Sludge,

After two previous admonitions in which I ordered you to separate charismatic seances both in time and in place from the celebration of Mass, I asked your Dean to ascertain whether my orders were being obeyed. I sent you his report on December 19th and repeated my orders:

1. Charismatic seances must not be held in the chapel;

2. Such seances must not be preceded or followed by any Eucharistic celebration whatsoever; the time gap between the two should be a minimum of two hours;

3. The Eucharistic celebration must take a form recognised by the Church and authorized by me.

To this letter I did not even receive the courtesy of an acknowledgement.

By my *Ad clerum* of January 13th I prohibited throughout the diocese the use of all personal innovations in the celebration of Mass.

Your letter dated last Monday, January 17th, makes it perfectly clear that:

1. You consider the ceremony witnessed by Dean McCarthy to be a Eucharist;

2. You will continue to celebrate it in that form no matter what I may say.

The position is consequently quite clear.

In view of which,

1. I cancel your appointment as chaplain to St Veronica's Convent at Horethorpe Hall;

2. I withdraw your diocesan faculties;

3. I suspend you *a divinis* until further notice.

I also order that you leave the premises of the Convent within three hours of this notification being handed to you by my representative, the Reverend Theodore Smith. You are to proceed to the Cathedral House at Stamford where the Administrator has a room at your disposal. He will then arrange for you to retire to a monastery for sufficient time for you to sort yourself out. Your personal belongings at Horethorpe will be delivered to the address you direct.

I further order that the keys of the chapel at Horethorpe, be they in the Sisters' or in your possession, be surrendered to Father Smith who will lock and seal the chapel. It must not be used until it has been exorcised and reblessed by me or my delegate nominated for that purpose. The Sisters and others who habitually use the chapel should attend Mass in the parish church at Horebury or elsewhere.

Father Theodore Smith is instructed to remain at the Convent until he is satisfied that my orders have been carried out.

Copies of this letter will be handed to the Sister Superior at Horethorpe and sent to the Mother Provincial and to Dean McCarthy.

Given at Stamford on this 20th day of January, 1977.

◇ ◇ ◇

I understand that Father Theodore Smith, the diocesan chucker-out, is a mountain of a man. Although only six foot six inches, he is disproportionately thick set and heavily boned. My informant writes: "He could lift Sludge in his left hand and flick him over the walls of Jericho slap into Rahab's lap."

As was to be expected, Father Sludge did not go to Cathedral House. What was unexpected was that he left not with one nun but with two.

Although it is out of chronological order since it is dated from the end of the following week, I here insert a letter from Bishop Forester to the Mother Provincial of the Veronican Sisters in order to close the Sludge incident.

14.   To the Very Reverend Mother Provincial
        Veronican Sisters, London.
Friday, January 28th, 1977.

Dear Mother Provincial,

A thousand thanks for your kind letter. But you must not blame yourself for the events at Horethorpe. If anyone is to blame it is I for leaving Sludge there for so long. Away back in the autumn of '75, not six months after his appointment, I got wind that he was up to strange tricks at ecumenical gatherings, along with an Anglican clergyman called Pyne-Pugh. I received a complaint from the village grocer in July to the effect that Mass at the Convent was a deal sight too rum for himself and the villagers, all of whom either went into Horebury or did not attend Mass at all. This Sludge dismissed as traditionalist resistance organized by the Latin Mass Society. Then a bit later there was that terrible indictment by the nun who jumped over the wall and whose name escapes me; as things have turned out, one could scarcely blame her. And so on.

Why did I let it go on for so long? I'll tell you. The reason is perfectly straightforward. How can one possibly call halt to others if one has not called halt to oneself? Let us be honest: until I had called a general halt, SLUDGE WAS IN THE RIGHT. The New Ordo IS an evolutionary ceremony. Its natural development IS the sort of thing that Sludge was doing. Swallow the New Ordo and you swallow Sludge.

The justification for the New Ordo is twofold: participation and ecumenism. Forget for a moment your dogma and your piety—your prejudices in fact—and take an objective look at Sludge's ceremony. It requires a total participation, in depth, down to all that is base in human nature. It is totally ecumenical, ambiguous to the point where the diabolic touches the divine. On grounds of participation and ecumenism, Sludge is right. Our contemporaries from the Pope downwards are constantly talking about "post-conciliar orientations," the new outlook. Well, an outlook looks out onto something. And what do we see? Sludge, Mother: Sludge is the outlook.

I can see the process at work among my fellow bishops. Several of them are very devout, very good men indeed; yet they allow the most astonishing things to be said and done in their dioceses. Why? Because they cannot stop the particular folly until they have cried a general halt—no more than I could stop Sludge before I had published my *Ad clerum* of January 13th.

In a lesser degree the same applies to the clergy. Had I dismissed Sludge a month ago my action would have been thought high-handed and unfair. Now it is applauded. Why? Because a halt has been called and if Sludge goes marching on, then he had better march out.

No, Mother Provincial, do not blame yourself. I do not even blame myself. I merely thank God that He has given me the grace to do what I have done.

Now for the practical side of your letter.

I entirely agree that Horethorpe has become a total white elephant to you. It is, moreover, a very valuable property. I disagree, however, the the Sludge scandal makes your presence in the diocese untenable. On the contrary, now is the time to hold your heads high. Why should the sordid follies of one man be allowed to blot out the devoted and noble work of all your nuns over a period of half a century?

I have a suggestion. For the moment it should be strictly confidential. If you agree to it, I shall reveal it in due course.

It is already quite clear to me that I have to reopen the diocesan seminary, closed in 1928. The old buildings here in Stamford have been turned into an old-folks home, for which they are admirably suited. I should not dream of turning the old folks out. I must consequently find another building. Horethorpe would be ideal. I suggest that my Trustees buy the whole estate off you at a price agreed by our clever surveyors. That is the first part of my proposition. It stands even if you refuse the second part.

This is the second part. The Hall alone would be quite large enough for the seminary. What about The Court? I suggest that you take it over as tenants from the Trust and look after the physical needs of the seminary. Moreover, if you ever have any more novices (as, pray God, you will), you could train them at the Court where the seminary clergy would be more likely to help than hinder their vocations. This implies, of course, that you, like me, will have to call a halt. Back to the holy Founder's rule! Back to your customary! Back to the habits which bred holiness! Back to the habit in which you were once proud to be clothed! I do not want any nuns running about the place in white slacks.

To cry halt will require courage—but more in perspective

53

than in fact. All fear is of the future, which is why we should never think of it. We should do what is right, upright, noble now, irrespective of what may follow. I assure you that, since I have taken the plunge, I have slept no worse than usual and am happier than I have been for years. You would not have to worry much about the shrieks of disapproval from Mother General in Rome. It is the diocesan bishops here who could make themselves unpleasant—but you would be unworthy of your sex if you failed to wheedle round them.

Anyway, you need not give me an immediate answer about taking over The Court and running the seminary. I should, however, be grateful to know if you will sell me the estate. I have the offer of a very fine site from the Dowager Duchess of Blackwater, but the house is rather small and I should have to build. The Duchess and I agree that Horethorpe would be preferable if you would sell it to us.

Cry halt and God bless you!

◇   ◇   ◇

The other two cases of direct opposition to Bishop Forester were less dramatic than that of the Reverend Roderic Sludge, although the first, judging by the Bishop's answer, was more pathetic.

15.　To a curate, aged 35, ordained in 1966.
Friday, January 21st, 1977.

Dear Father,

How sad! How sad! My heart bleeds for you. You were the first priests I ordained, at Pentecost 1966. What a good-looking young fellow you were. You were wonderfully fresh and new and innocent, like a butterfly just out of its cocoon. But it was 1966. The landslide had started. It turned into an avalanche. You were uprooted, lost all your certitudes. And look at you now! It is not your fault. I blame you for nothing. You are the victim of shallow minds and crooked hearts. That is how I see it.

You see it exactly the other way round. I am quite dumbfounded by your second paragraph. "When you ordained me, I could see a Church full of hope, where the old martinetism would give way to freedom, the religion of fear to one of love; where the priest could take his place in the world on an equal footing with his neighbour; where married priests seemed round the corner and we could bear the burden and enjoy the solace of family life; where the dogmas which no one believes would cease to be a barrier between men of good will. Well, I still clung to my hope until your *Ad clerum.* That is the end. You who ordained me have slammed the door in my face." Do you mean to tell me that on that fatal day the Mass, Jesus, His Blessed Mother, the ineffable Trinity, the adoration which is God's due—none of this crossed your mind? That all you thought of was freedom, love, social status, family life and general benevolence?

No, Father, that is not what you felt at Pentecost 1966. It has taken many years for the good wine to turn to vinegar. But I see what you mean, all right: your ideals have been disillusioned, your hopes frustrated, your ambitions thwarted. This, I imagine, is true enough. But if somehow you could rediscover what were those ideals, hopes and ambitions, you would find them different from what you say; and you have been disillusioned, frustrated and thwarted precisely because you have lost them.

Dare I ask you to come and see me? I fear that you will only jeer at the suggestion.

Anyway, to come to your formal request, the answer is: NO. I am dead against laicization. You do not have to answer to me, my dear Father; you have to answer to God. You have undertaken obligations and made vows to God, not to me. It is perfectly possible that you did so under a misapprehension or that circumstances have made them untenable. God can see and judge that, not I. What does laicization do? It merely respectabilizes the situation; it does not alter it. This "respectabilization" I hate. I honour a man who shoulders his responsibilities, even if I disapprove of his actions. I have nothing but contempt for the man who shirks them or shovels them off in an attempt at self-justification. You have been a priest long enough, my dear Father, to know that self-justification is the only sin which even God cannot justify.

You do not mention if there is a woman involved. I presume that there is or you would have said that there was not. Curiously enough, I blame you all the less. What does a man need from a woman? Physical sex, doubtless. But in and beyond that he wants reassurance, rehabilitation, the renewal of energy to face the world. A woman recharges our drained battery. We priests used to get all that from our Spouse, the Church. Celibacy used not to be difficult because the Church gave us more than any human wife could give. But now? Well, I no longer blame you although I know that you are utterly and hopelessly wrong.

Obviously I pray and beg that you will not disappear on the date you say but I thank you for the warning. I shall keep it secret as you request. If you disappear, however, you can introduce me one day to your mistress but never to your wife: I know her already—she is the Church.

◇   ◇   ◇

16.   To the Reverend William Harris, aged 42.
   Parish Priest of a one-horse suburban parish.
Friday, January 21st, 1977.

Dear Father,
   I wish all correspondents were as succinct as you and that I could answer as succinctly. Just one sentence: "Kindly transfer me to a diocese in which the Bishop has not gone bats." It has cheered me up for the day.

   I am well aware that, just as some priests play golf, your particular hobby is to knock off a new Mass-form before you go to bed for use the following morning. The hobby is doubtless innocent enough but you have no right to inflict the result on the Faithful. Hence, it is inevitable that you should conform or that we should part. Obviously I should prefer the first alternative, not out of a spirit of domination but because you are one of the few 'progressives' in the diocese whom I positively like. You do not invent your ridiculous ceremonies because of some dull theory but from sheer *joie de vivre*. They consequently do little harm although they cannot be allowed.

   Incidentally, I have just got rid of poor Father Sludge. He was the sort of progressive whom I found intolerable: all theory and no life, no guts but all gall. I should hate to class you in his category.

   Could not you try the old Mass? You know, it gives far more internal, spiritual freedom than the new—if only because it is silent. The diocesan guru has accepted it, much to his P.P.'s surprise. What I am getting at is this: I suspect that

56

your hobby is due to the inadequacy of the New Ordo. Presented with a ridiculous ceremony, you might as well try your hand at making one less ridiculous: hence the hobby. The old Mass, on the other hand, is never ridiculous. If it errs it is in being too majestic, too colossal—but that may be because we moderns are such pygmies. Try it, Father. You certainly have not said it for over six years and probably for over ten. Say it at first on a weekday when you have time, rolling the lapidary sentences round your tongue as you would good wine: *"tibique reddunt vota sua, aeterno Deo vivo et vero."*

You see, it is perfectly clear that the episcopal brethren are bound to react to the situation brought about by my *Ad clerum.* And how will they react? I do not know much more than you. That is why you will have to be patient. I imagine that one or two may follow in my footsteps, even though hesitantly and in keeping their distance. They would not do for you: you might fall from the frying pan into the fire. The hard-line progressives are likely to harden in defence of the New Ordo and take a dim view of your hobby. So they will not do either. What you need is a gentle, soppy bishop who is a bit bats—somebody exactly like me. But you assure me that I won't do. Much patience will therefore be required.

There is hope, however. In this, the first week of my *Ad clerum*, I have received exactly twenty-two requests from priests of other dioceses to be incardinated into Stamford. Obviously I have put them all off in as kindly a fashion as I can. In time, however, I may discover that one or more are perfectly sound priests, unchipped, unsullied, uninebriate, who really are suffering at the hands of their Father in God for no other reason than that they cling to the Old Religion— in much the same way as you are suffering at my hands for the Religion of Tomorrow. It might be possible to swap priests as in the good old days one did slaves. I am not saying that I should not be sorry to lose you; I should. But under such circumstances my episcopal colleague might be delighted to receive you—a point not immaterial to your future happiness.

Patience, Father, patience! And try the Immemorial Mass.

◇   ◇   ◇

17.   To the Clerical Students of the Diocese.

Of the five students, two had been sent to a seminary which had since closed and been amalgamated with a theological college attached to London University. One of these was due to receive the priesthood in 1977, the other the diaconate. The remaining three were younger and had been sent to a Northern seminary.

Dear Messrs Parker, Baldock and Company,

I intended to write to you but you have forestalled me. And with what wonderful letters! As you have written on behalf of your fellow students as well as yourselves, I shall answer you all with this one epistle.

I am overjoyed to hear your reaction to my *Ad clerum.* I was very nervous, especially, Mr Parker, on your account, as you are already a deacon. Let me answer your personal question straight away; no, I do not intend to postpone your ordination unless you so wish it.

What I propose to do is to ordain you (Parker) priest and Mr. Evans deacon; from the North, Mr Baldock, sub-deacon; and give the tonsure and First Minors to Messrs Carr and Thwaites. All this on the Vigil of Pentecost, May 28th, here in the Cathedral. On Whitsunday the Cathedral High Mass can then be celebrated by Fr Parker with the Revds Evans and Baldock as deacon and sub-deacon and Messrs Carr and Thwaites performing their respective functions. I hope this meets with your approval. We can arrange quite easily to put your people up overnight at Stamford.

The ordination and the High Mass will, of course, be according to the Immemorial Rite. I suggest that during the Easter holidays you spend a couple of days at Cathedral House so that the Administrator can show you what to do. I doubt if anybody at your present establishments remembers anything about it. I also want all of you to make your pre-ordination retreat from the evening of Sunday, May 22nd at Cathedral House.

I am most struck by the fact that all five of you agree that your present formation is inadequate and at all events at variance with the spirit of the *Ad clerum.* This seems to me to be true. But it is too early for me to decide how to remedy the situation. Both your letters say that the *Ad clerum* has electrified your respective establishments and that I could empty them tomorrow if I opened "a real seminary." Perhaps, but it is not feasible. If I attempted to snatch even a couple of students from other dioceses I should quite naturally incur the implacable enmity of every bishop in the land. Moreover, what hope would there be of a return to religious sanity throughout the country if all right-minded young priests were huddled together in the little diocese of Stamford? It won't do. You must encourage your companions (whom God bless) to preserve their priestly ideals, possibly by forming an association, with a view to spreading religious sanity in the diverse dioceses to which they belong.

On the other hand, in this the first week, I have applications from ten ex-students who left their seminaries disillusioned but would return to a traditional one were I to open it. I also have letters from fifteen young men who wish to try their vocations. During the next few weeks the number in each category may have doubled. But what does it mean? I do not know—except that I shall have to interview a refreshingly large number of young men.

Anyway, after Pentecost you will have to return to your respective establishments until the end of the Summer Term. Father Parker and Revd Evans can be used during the summer holidays if they so wish. I guarantee, however, to have as suitable a set-up as numbers allow in September. Father Parker will be able to do a post-ordination course while helping out in other ways. Incidentally, I shall not send you abroad because I believe that the native clergy should breathe their native fog.

I add this note specifically for Messrs Evans and Baldock. Mr Evans, you have not been ordained sub-deacon because that order has been suppressed in the post-conciliar Church. It is, indeed, of ecclesiastical, not of divine origin. As you did not receive it when it was due, I shall not give it to you at Pentecost. You will be ordained straight to the diaconate. Mr Baldock, you are due for the sub-diaconate so I shall revive the order in this diocese and first in your favour. Now, it is in view of the sub-diaconate (but in your case, Mr Evans, of the diaconate) that you make your vows of celibacy. I want your assurance that you understand this perfectly. You also understand that it is a private vow which you make directly to God and from which no human authority can dispense you. The Pope can use "the Power of the Keys" but strictly speaking that is not a dispensation. Your bride will be the Church and you will have none other.

I shall write no more about it now but shall have something to say concerning the nobility of vows in general and the sublimity of that of chastity in particular during your pre-ordination retreat.

I thank you all from the bottom of my heart. May God bless you and do you pray for. . . .

◇　◇　◇

In the above letter to his clerical students, Bishop Forester mentions ten applications from ex-students and fifteen from other young men to join the diocesan clergy. From the correspondence I notice that there were also eight applications from "late vocations." All these were meticulously if summarily answered and appointments for interviews were given. There is no point in publishing them. In explanation for the wideness of this response, it must be remembered that the national press reported fairly, even favourably on the Ad clerum *in their issues of Monday, January 17th. His Lordship was also interviewed on radio and television. The Catholic weeklies, of course, only go to press on Wednesday night, so there was as yet no coverage from that source.*

It was doubtless the reaction of his clerical students and the obvious quality of some of the applicants which induced Bishop Forester to write the following letter.

18.　To Monsignor Charles Bouverie, D.D.
　　　St Vitus' Mental Home, Epsom.
Friday, January 21st, 1977.

Dear Monsignor,

I have followed your career with deep admiration: Vice-rector of the English College; Rector of the Diocesan Orphanage; Parish Priest of Thistleford (a dump I know well, as I was once P. P. of Grumby not twenty miles away); chaplain to the Sisters at Hogsholt; and now assistant chaplain at a lunatic asylum. Everyone knows why. There is no more honourable career in the Universal Church.

I also wish to express my profound admiration for the three publications of yours which I have read. Your book entitled *Four Abbots* on Chautard, Marmion, Chapman and Vonier is admirable. Your two long essays on "The Direct Perception of God" and "The Mechanism of Prayer" are splendid. You are the man I want.

I enclose an *Ad clerum* which I issued a week ago. You may have seen reports of it in the papers. Now, it seems to me inevitable that I shall have to re-open the diocesan seminary. I only have five senior students at the moment but, even now in the first week, I have over thirty applicants of varying ages and backgrounds: ten ex-seminarians, fifteen new vocations between 17 and 21, eight between 23 and 55. On paper twelve seem admirable and only three more than doubtful. I need two things: firstly, expert opinion in interviewing these men; secondly, if a reasonable number of them—say six or more—seem suitable, a Rector for my seminary. Are you interested? Incidentally, I have given no appointments for interview before the weekend of January 29/30th, so that you may be present to advise me if you so wish.

I shall also want to discuss with you the curriculum. The old system had enormous merits and I am deeply grateful for what I received at my seminary. Nevertheless it is abundantly clear that the system has FAILED—yes, in capitals. Every bishop, every priest had been through a seminary course. Every bishop, every priest came away convinced that he had the answer to every question. It only required that this attitude be dubbed "triumphalism" and to suggest that questions are meant to be asked, not answered, for every bishop and every priest to be left dumbfounded. We lacked the techniques to question the questions and still tried to give answers which nobody wanted. Moreover, our certitudes were closely bound to a given set of symbols. Change the well defined Latin term for an undefined Greek one and every bishop and every priest found himself at a loss. We knew the catechism by heart; mention catechesis and we are no longer sure who made us and why. We could manage a dogmatic sermon all right but just listen to our homilies! We were absolutely firm about confession and contrition; all our firmness vanished at the one word *metanoia*. We knew exactly what the Mass was; the Eucharist is hazy. Even the Consecration and the Real Presence have been engulfed in the mist of *anamnesis*. All this is patently true, is undeniable. We had received a solid theological training in our seminaries. It did not stand the test. It collapsed overnight without leaving track or trace. It requires explanation.

I am not saying that the seminaries were to blame for the collapse. This would be quite untrue; there are other causes. What I am saying is that there must have been some lacuna in the system which rendered the whole edifice vulnerable. That it lay in the seminaries is certain, since they provided the only ground common to every priest and every bishop. What was it?

It is quite clear that we all believed in the Trinity; in the Incarnation, Resurrection and Ascension of Our Lord; in the Seven Sacraments working *ex opere operato*; in the Immaculate Conception and the Assumption and so on. Yes, we all believed in them but apparently in a disembodied sort of way, as abstract propositions not as immediate realities. An abstract proposition can be more or less true according to the available data; realities cannot change because they are the data. Unless I am talking complete nonsense, the problem thus becomes: how is it that our seminaries failed to translate the abstract propositions of the Faith into an immediate reality? Worse still: how is it that students who arrived with the realities of their catechism soon found them evaporated into abstract propositions?

I think there is an explanation. The translation of an abstract proposition into the reality of Faith comes about on the divine side by grace but in the human response by one means only: prayer. As far as I know, there was not a seminary in the world which included in its curriculum a course on prayer: its physics, metaphysics and theology. Spiffs by spiritual directors and petty devotions are no substitute. To my mind, the first year at a senior seminary should be devoted almost exclusively to the philosophy, theology and practice of prayer. Incidentally, when I say "practice" I do not mean that they should be made to pray, because it cannot be done, but that they should be made acquainted with how it has been done from the lapidary sentences of the Desert Fathers, through the great mystics, medieval and otherwise, down to your Four Abbots. Also, I say "almost exclusively" because a little history and general culture would relieve the tension. That is why I want you. It is clear from your publications that you have the ideas and ideals which seem to me necessary. And my opinion of your publications was not belied on the couple of occasions when I had the pleasure of meeting you.

Incidentally, I have not the slightest doubt but that prayer is the fundamental lacuna in the clergy today. One only has to look at Vatican II. There were a couple of thousand bishops, all honourable men, discussing pastoral problems. The only subject which failed to get a mention was the one which most concerned their flock; prayer. Why? Because it never crossed their minds; it is the great lacuna. Later the New Ordo was produced: it is a function designed for participation but not for prayer. One can function it all right, but precisely in the measure that it is functional it is unprayable. That is the trouble: for many years now the seminaries having been churning out functionaries, ecclesiastical civil servants, instead of men of prayer, priests of God.

There are also several purely pedagogic problems which I want to discuss with you. Do you know that I went through my whole seminary course without having seriously to put pen to paper? Just end-of-term examinations as a test of memory, that was all. I consequently never had to think but merely remember. And I wonder how many priests have actually read a single work by one of the Fathers or Doctors of the Church? Now that they no longer say the breviary, their ignorance in that direction must be simply appalling.

Yes, I want to revive the diocesan seminary. I want our perennial philosophy and theology to be taught therein. I also want the lacunae to be filled.

Please come to see me as soon as you conveniently can. Please accept the Rectorship as I feel sure that we shall agree on the curriculum.

Monsignor Bouverie appears to have arrived at Stamford on Friday, January 28th and to have interviewed a number of students on Saturday and Sunday. The curriculum was discussed. He accepted the Rectorship of the seminary, provided suitable premises could be found.

REGULAR CLERGY and CONVENTS OF RELIGIOUS WOMEN

No useful purpose would be served in publishing Bishop Forester's letters to the Regular clergy. The stable orders—Cassianese Benedictines, Cistercians (unreformed) and Canons Regular, all of whom served parishes in their neighbourhoods—were more than delighted to comply with the Bishop's wishes. The Provincials of movable orders and congregations were equally delighted to have somewhere to dump their traditionalist members. Only the Reparationist Fathers, notorious for their advanced views, proved obdurate. The bishop withdrew their diocesan faculties, and, as will be seen later, they left diocese.

The thirty-four convents of women were a very different matter. They received a great deal of care and attention from Bishop Forester which will be dealt with in a separate chapter.

THE LAITY

From Wednesday, January 19th, onwards, letters poured in at the rate of over two hundred a day. Few seem to have been critical and of these most expressed indignation that His Lordship had not suppressed the New Ordo altogether and reimposed the Leonine prayers at the end of Mass. The overwhelming majority showed their appreciation of Bishop Forester's stand in the one way open to them by enclosing money.

To cope with this situation two lay secretaries were employed and the Diocesan Treasurer was made to surrender a member of his staff, the indefatigable Miss Defew, niece of the Administrator.

Inevitably, almost all the letters to the laity were stereotyped acknowledgements with a kindly word in the handwriting of a secretary. Some, however, had to be answered by His Lordship in person. I quote one because of its eventual importance.

19.   To Selina, Duchess of Blackwater
     The Old Hall, Blackwater.

The Dowager Duchess is still a relatively young woman, under sixty. Her husband was killed in the Dieppe landing shortly after the birth of the present Duke. She has not remarried. She was received into the Church in 1952. The Duchess has never hidden her religious convictions. When her parish priest attempted to persuade her to attend the New Mass in the parish church on the grounds of example, she replied in front of a whole roomful of witnesses: "I should be giving an example of hypocrisy. Is that what you want? Besides, no bishop, not even that of Rome, will induce me to swallow my vomit."

Friday, January 21st, 1977.

Dear Duchess,

Since Tuesday, when I acknowledged your incredibly generous gift of £5,000, money has been rolling in, from £1 notes slipped into an envelope to substantial cheques, including another gift of £5,000, of which more anon. To date, Miss Defew has banked altogether £23,428. It is staggering.

But it presents a problem. The money is not a gift to the diocese of Stamford but is clearly intended for the perpetuation of the Immemorial Religion in general and the Mass in particular. Every letter, from the most humble to the most grand, contains some such sentence as: "I have not been to Mass for x years. Here is the money I would have put in the plate." Or, "I refuse to pay for goods I don't want so I haven't given a penny to the Church since . . ."; that sort of thing. And this not merely from the diocese but from all over the British Isles. It is obviously imperative that this money should be spent according to the implied intentions of the donors.

How can this be done? For the moment I have opened an account called the Tridentine Trust in the joint names of Father FitzHenry and myself. But this is purely temporary. What is wanted is a properly constituted trust composed of well known traditionalists to administer the sums put at its disposal. In view of the fact that the powers that be can exercise pressure on the clergy far more easily than on the laity, the majority of members of the trust should be lay. I am thinking in terms of five laymen to three clergymen, so that even if a layman dies the laity still have a majority.

Whom have I got in mind?

The chairman is quite obvious: the Dowager Duchess of Blackwater. Sir John Cutting, the judge, also seems to me obvious. He, too, sent quite a sizable cheque despite the fact that he is still educating some of his numerous progeny.

Cyril Outman, the chairman of the County Council, is surely inevitable. He may be a bit domineering but he has the Faith and is no fool—far from it. Besides, his bulk impresses.

Then, from outside the diocese, I suggest the chairman for the time being of the Latin Mass Society. I see no reason why he should not be in a position to dip into our funds, since the money comes from all over the country.

For the last of the laymen, Mr Solly Glauben. Don't jump! Yes, the Jew "barrow-boy to millionaire." I shall explain in a moment.

The three clerics would be myself, as an individual, not *ex officio* as Bishop of Stamford; Bryan Houghton, whom you know; and probably a Monsignor Charles Bouverie, whom you don't. Concerning Fr H., I realize that he lives in France but he can always come over to England for important meetings and can be consulted by phone or post. As for Bouverie, he used to be vice-rector of the English College and is now assistant chaplain at a lunatic asylum on account of the Mass. He is likely to be a big spender out of the trust—but I shall tell you all about that by word of mouth. If not Bouverie, I shall have to find someone else, but not a priest of the diocese as the temptation to use the fund for parochial purposes would be too great.

Now back to Solly Glauben. It is he who has sent the other cheque for £5,000, along with a very long manuscript letter presumably so that no secretary would see it. Some of it is indeed confidential. However, the passage on his conversion, no matter how personal, is not really confidential, so I enclose photocopies of it. Is not his handwriting unexpected, rather large, untidy and with lots of curious idiosyncrasies? One would take it for that of an artist rather than of a financial wizard.

Now, my dear Duchess, read the photocopies. The date is 1963 when Glauben was 22.

The Photocopies:

I was a practicing, pious Jew, with all the fervour of which a young man is capable. I loved the Law and clung to it as the vine to the fig tree. Yet I was assailed by a terrible doubt: we, the Chosen People, seemed pathetically faithful to the Covenant; it was God who seemed faithless. Away with the thought: His faithfulness endures forever! Yes, that was the basis of all my piety: God's faithfulness endures, whatever the human appearances. Then one day, suddenly like lightning on Lebanon, it struck me (not as ideas strike but as lightning strikes) that if the Covenant had been voided it was because God in His faithfulness had Himself filled the void. If the Sacrifice of the Covenant had been abolished it could only be because God in His faithfulness had sacrificed Himself. In a flash, as a Jew, I found myself a Catholic. I am a convert to the Sacrificial Presence of God Incarnate in the Mass.

I was in the Midlands at the time, working in a small factory which belonged to an uncle. I knew no Catholic priest. I called round at the presbytery and took pot luck. The priest who instructed me was an astonishing fellow, although I did not recognize it at the time. I thought all priests were as like as peas in a pod. He disapproved of the mass media, took no paper and possessed neither radio or television. Although a man of immense culture, he paid not the slightest attention to what was going on around him. His instructions were magnificent. I was duly received into the Church on December 8th, 1963. I stayed on in the Midlands until the New Year. It was a month in heaven.

But how could I tell my family? How could I bring shame and sorrow on my dear father's head? I decided to change my name and to lose myself in London where nobody knew me. I chose the name 'Glauben' partly because it sounds Jewish and I am proud to be a Jew, partly because it is the German for faith. Thus I arrived in London, penniless and nameless but with the Faith.

It did not take me more than a month in London to discover that I had not been received but deceived into the Church. The God of my Midland priest had been the God of Israel, totally transcendent, totally "other." The Covenant was, is and ever shall be the Incarnation. The Incarnation was consummated on the Cross, is consummated at Mass and

67

ever shall be in "the Lamb to whom all saving power belongs." All this I could understand. It is the apotheosis of Jewry.

And what did I find in London? I found an idolatry worse than that of Baal or Moloch, which were at least "other" than man; a faithlessness worse than atheism, which at least knows what it denies. I found the Catholic Church rotten with the nadir of idolatry and the zenith of blasphemy: religious humanism, the identification of God with man. No transcendent God, no Covenant, no Incarnation, no Mass. And they talk about ecumenism, when even a totem-worshipper would not accept such faithlessness.

I had rejected the Synagogue one month; the next I was rejected by the Church. I did not lose my faith. We Jews are used to exile. I simply hung up my harp, as it were, by the waters of Babylon.

I have not practiced since my first month in London. Apart from my dear wife (also a convert Jewess) and my two lovely children (who are too young to understand), few people know that I am a Catholic. But if you, Bishop, can restore to me my month of heaven, then all the world shall know and all my fortune is at your disposal.

Does that give you a sufficient picture of Solly Glauben? I find it very moving. And the reactions ring true. "Deceived into the Church," what a terrible indictment! And it must have happened umpteen thousands of times. God forgive me!

To return to your being chairman of the Trust, please ring me up if you approve and agree. I shall tell Canon Cocksedge to put you through.

68

CHAPTER III

THE COUNTER-BOMB

20. To the Reverend Bryan Houghton,
Avignon, France.

*(It should be remembered that at this date Bishop Forester
had not yet sent me the copies of his letters. He therefore
describes some of the events of the week in considerable
detail. I shall omit passages which refer to what is already
well known to the reader. It is clear from the typing errors—which I have let stand—that this letter was not dic-
tated.)*

Saturday, January 22nd, 1977.

Dear Bryan,

So that is the first week over. It has been gruelling. Socks,
of course, has taken it in his stride but Fitz and I are absolutely exhausted.

How has it gone?

Splendidly, as I thought until an hour ago when the enemy exploded its counter-bomb. I never expected it. I am far
more upset than I should be. But of that anon. I had better
tell you the events as they struck me.

In the first place, the Cardinal has promised me his benevolent neutrality. This is much more than I had expected. It cheers me up to remind myself of it by telling you. And I think he is sincere and solid. The enemy bomb will leave him unmoved.

Testastorta wrote as foreseen from the Delegation. It is more than likely that it is who [sic] has laid the counter-bomb.

Then I had letters from five of my episcopal brethren. One, Blythe (Birkenhead), was enthusiastic and promised to follow in my footsteps. But will he now? The other four disagree but do not oppose. Derby was as rude as usual but I suspect that he was trying to be nice. And what of the other fourteen diocesan bishops who did not write? Apart from the two hard-line progressives at Halifax and Taunton, I presume they are waiting to follow their leader as soon as they know who the leader is to be. In the meantime they are exercising the virtue of prudence. Anyway, that was all fairly satisfactory. You see, we bishops form a sort of club and the first reaction is to be decent to a fellow member—unless he is a complete cad and lets the side down. I rather feared I had and am delighted to discover that I am still O.K.

I was a little disappointed in the clergy, however. I probably expected too much. They are punch-drunk from all they have had to put up with over the past dozen years. True, there has been very little open opposition but the V.G. and Socks both tell me that there is a fair amount of moaning and groaning beneath the surface. That does not surprise me. What does is that I only received twelve letters of enthusiastic support. I had expected—and indeed need—more to get things going properly. However, the clergy hate writing so I may have been lucky to get any letters at all.

The laity, on the other hand, have been absolutely wonderful. Last Sunday, here at the Cathedral . . .

(There follows a description of lay enthusiasm similar to that in Letter 8 but with the addition of details from other churches in the diocese. The enormous mail from the laity, enclosing money, is dealt with in much the same way as in Letter 19 to the Duchess of Blackwater, as is also the need to form a properly constituted Trust to administer the funds. I am asked to act as one of the Trustees, which I of course accepted.)

. . . So that is how things stood until this morning. I must frankly admit that I thought they were going pretty well. I was finishing my breakfast when Socks came in with the Catholic papers. "Have a look at this," he said. It was front page news. "DYING BISHOP OPPOSES POPE. Bishop Forester of Stamford, whose health has been causing anxiety for some time, has issued a Pastoral Letter which will cause dismay to every thinking Catholic. As is well known, Bishop Forester suffers from an inoperable cancer and is not expected to live long. He has chosen such a moment, when other thoughts might seem more appropriate, to ban the New Order of Mass in his diocese and reimpose the forbidden Mass of Pius V . . . He consulted neither the other bishops of England and Wales nor his Holiness the Pope . . . It is feared that his health has upset the balance of his mind . . . The priests of the diocese are in an uproar . . . Interviewed outside the Cathedral of Stamford last Sunday, a typical parishoner said: 'I never back a horse which cannot stay the course' . . . etc . . . etc . . . It is understood that the Holy See will ask Bishop Forester to resign on the grounds of ill health."

Now, Bryan, as you are well aware, I had told only two people that I had cancer: Socks and yourself. As far as I was concerned nobody else knew. How had the press got hold of it? I asked Socks. He pointed out that dozens of people knew: my doctor, a couple of specialists, the radiologist, a gaggle of nurses and filing secretaries, and probably anybody who really wanted to find out. I had never thought of it. But of course he is right. How stupid can one be?

It changes the whole situation. Everybody, bishops, clergy, laity will have at the back of their minds that horrid little couplet:

I never back a horse
Which cannot stay the course.

Nobody knows the length of the course or my staying power— but they will not think of that. In actual fact, given enough support from the clergy, the course need not be longer than from now to Easter. By then sufficient could be done to make it difficult to undo. As for my staying power, Professor Phillips told me last August that, provided I took life calmly, I could expect anything between 9 and 18 months of normal activity and then I might get into trouble. Actually, I have got a bit of trouble now but little pain, thank God!—but I shall not be coming to Avignon this summer.

I have been discussing the whole question with Socks between breakfast and now. As usual, he is totally unflappable, totally objective, totally insensitive. He takes a dim view of things. He thinks the articles really have spiked my gun. Not a bishop nor a priest will follow me; as for the laity, their disillusionment would leave them more hopeless than had they never hoped. I asked him straight: "So you think I should resign?" He shrugged his shoulders and said: "Unfortunately you cannot deny the basic truth of the articles."

But, Bryan, I won't. What is right is right, whether I have ten minutes or ten years to live. I shall see this business through so long as God gives me life. The fact that I am cut off will not shorten God's arm and while I live I cannot escape being an instrument in His hand. Too long, too long I have acted according to human prudence. At last I shall act according to Divine Prudence which men call folly.

I am quite determined on that score. What rather daunts me is that I shall have to start all over again. The new situation will produce new reactions. And all this because what everybody knew has become news: Edmund Forester is mortal! Worst of all, I shall have to endure a thousand inquiries after my health.

You will say a Mass for me, won't you? To me it is the only reality in all the world. The Hidden Presence is the only Real Presence; all the rest are only appearances. And when I do die, you will come over to tuck me up? I should hate other hands than yours to commit me to God. I shall leave instructions to that effect.

Anyway, that's that.

I shall not answer the Catholic papers. Why should I? I shall have to write an *Ad clerum* to tell the clergy that what they say is true but has nothing to do with what is right and wrong. I do not feel calm enough to do it now.

—Fitz has just been. He had tears in his eyes and knelt before me for my blessing. He is a good boy, both sensitive and sensible. But I wish people would not expect me to console them; it is sufficient to have to console myself.—

I shall write the *Ad clerum* tomorrow after Mass and shall send you a copy.

◊　◊　◊

72

21. *Ad clerum.*

Ad clerum 77-2
Sunday, January 23rd, 1977.

Right Reverend, Very Reverend and Reverend Fathers,

The Catholic press has seen fit to publicize the fact that I suffer from cancer and am unlikely to live long. Whence it derived its information is a mystery to me. I had kept the matter, as I thought, completely secret as being of little interest to anybody but myself. The Catholic press thinks otherwise. Why? It is not out of concern for my immortal soul. It is because

"It never backs a horse
Which cannot stay the course"

and wishes to make sure that you, the clergy of the diocese, will not do so either.

The merits or defects of my *Ad clerum* of January 13th are not discussed. Whether it is right or wrong is not considered. It is purely a matter of expedience: the existing bishop will not stay the course and you will have a new bishop chosen expressly to undo whatever he has done. Such is the message.

In a way I am grateful for it. Death is so mysterious a phenomenon that the nearer one gets to it the less real it seems. I am inclined to forget it, it is so near. The press has kindly reminded me that there is a certain urgency in pressing forward my design. The specialist assures me that I am likely to die between May of this year and February of next. It is, of course, not certain; besides, I may die of something different in the meantime. However, in the normal course of events I am in the enviable position of having some idea of my death-day, albeit less accurately than of my birthday.

Now, I wish to make it quite clear that the contingency of my death will not affect my actions during life. I shall do what I consider right and upright whether I have ten minutes or ten years to live. This means that I shall not resign the diocese nor withdraw the *Ad clerum.* On the contrary, I shall go about my business with added urgency, prompted by the proximity of death. What happens after my death is no concern of mine. All I know is that God's arm will not be shortened because I am cut off.

But what of you, my dear Fathers? It is easy enough for me to play the hero precisely because I shall die and leave you to face the consequences. This is true. It is therefore now that you will have to decide whether to act according to what you consider right or according to what is expedient. That in itself will not be too easy. Far more difficult, however, is that you will have to start considering now your whole attitude to obedience. Let us suppose that you obey me now and give me your enthusiastic support in restoring the immemorial Church, will you, from the same obedience, destroy it with equal enthusiasm under my successor?

To appeal to obedience is a snare and self-delusion. Obedience does not exonerate us from our moral responsibility. Quite certainly obedience should never be blind. We always obey something, be it the Commandments of God, our passions, indolence or fear. We must keep our eyes wide open to make sure which it is we are obeying. That is a particular trouble in times of revolution, such as the one in which we live: authority becomes uncertain; it is arbitrary; it speaks with an ambiguous voice; at one moment it thunders, at the next it whines; the Rule of Law gives place to countless administrative injunctions; as authority weakens the administration takes over. In a revolution it is inevitable that if you obey one thing, you disobey another. Thus, if you obey me, you will disobey my successor—who is only a few months away. If you obey my successor, who does not exist, you are disobeying me who do. To appeal to obedience is consequently ridiculous. It will not do. With your eyes wide open, quite deliberately, you will have to decide whether you believe in the Revelation handed down to you by the tradition, testimony and authority of the Church, as expressed in its formularies, or whether you believe in an evolving religion which emerges from your own self-expression. The choice is between orthodoxy and orthopraxis: i.e. is the Church infallible in her Faith, or impeccable in her actions? Having made your decision, you will have to stand by the consequences. Thus, Fathers, I do not appeal for your obedience and loyalty. I appeal to your Faith and rely on your heroism.

Mind you, in the last paragraph I have put everything logically, in black and white, as we human beings are bound to do. We know, however that God's Providence never works logically. Some ridiculous detail will act as a prism so that the choice of black and white is transformed into a rainbow, the promise that we shall not be engulfed in the flood. But you must be prepared. You must already have made up your minds before I die. You will then have no need of me. It is I who shall need your prayers.

During the following week Bishop Forester received letters of inquiry and sympathy concerning his health from all the members of the English Hierarchy, from a great many of his priests and from countless lay folk. Where acknowledgement was necessary it was made by means of a printed card:

Bishop Edmund Forester wishes to thank you for your kind inquiry after his health. His cancer is inconvenient but not painful. The specialist is of the opinion that it is unlikely to become serious for several months.

He asks for your prayers and sends you his blessing.

This card was also enclosed with most of his letters so as to relieve him of having to write about a subject which bored him.

22.   Second letter to Charles Blythe, Bishop of Birkenhead. *(The first is #3.)*
Monday, January 24th, 1977.

Dear Charles,
   Yes, it is perfectly true but the pundits still give me several months. It is inconvenient rather than painful; the pills keep it under control. No, it does not worry me in the least. In fact it seems to worry you much more than it does me.
   Charles, I am shocked to the core of my being. You rang up on the morning of Saturday 15th. Canon Cocksedge assured me that you were enthusiastic and intended to follow suit. The same day you wrote to me rather more guardedly: you intended to use the Indult to its utmost limit. Now, it is the New Ordo in Latin. What pain my cancer gives you! Doubtless, too, you are medicated by that clever physician, Dr Testastorta. I may have cancer in my guts but you seem to have no guts at all.
   I shall deal with the points in your letter in the same order as you:

75

1. "The issue is really only one of language." No, it is not and you know it. Between 1965 and Advent 1970 we had the Old Rite in pidgin English. It would not do. No matter how bad the translation the theocentric sacrifice still shone through. The Old Rite remained clearly participation with God through Jesus Christ. What was wanted was something anthropocentric: participation with men in the name of Jesus—"when two or three are gathered together . . ." The Old and New Rite are differently "oriented," to use an expression dear to Paul VI.

2. "There is no reason why the New Ordo should not be said in Latin." Yes, there is, and you know it.

   a) The New Ordo is intended for the vernacular. The only law on the subject says so (the Constitution of April 1969). Apart from a passage in the text, the penultimate paragraph reads: ". . . by its assistance (the N.O.'s) one and the same prayer shall ascend from all people in a vast variety of languages (*in tot varietate linguarum*) to the Heavenly Father . . ." Note, it is a prayer, not a sacrifice, and should be recited by the people in their own tongue. You will consequently be disobeying the intention if not the letter of the law, although you will certainly be obeying Testastorta.

   b) If the New Ordo is said in Latin it loses its only justification: meaningful participation. It therefore becomes unjustified. If said in Latin, then it is clear to all that it was not introduced for pastoral participation but for DOCTRINAL reasons. I repeat: if the New Ordo is considered acceptable in Latin, then the motive for imposing it cannot have been pastoral and must have been doctrinal. You, Charles Blythe, will be admitting that the doctrine of the Mass has changed. You will, however, have done one good deed: you will have thrown off the cloak of hypocrisy in which the N.O. has been clothed.

3. "When the New Rite is sung in Latin there is no question of the sacrifice of the Mass being replaced by a meal." Charles, how can you write such nonsense? Since when has singing turned a meal into a sacrifice? I know what you mean, of course, but it does not work. I shall give you an example from my diocese.

Last June, while I was in hospital, there died a priest called Roy Burns. Actually he had been a bitter progressive and a more painful thorn than cancer in my side. However, he left instructions that he was to have a Tridentine Requiem under his Indult. His Dean, by no means a bad chap, duly celebrated the Immemorial Rite, but facing the people and with five co-celebrants. Vernacular hymns were sung throughout, except when a sort of compere or conductor chatted away while the congregation was gathering its breath for another hymn. None but an expert could have diagnosed the Old Rite. My evidence is unquestionable. Incidentally, the Dean doubtless pocketed the stipend of £100 contingent on the celebration of the Tridentine Mass. Do you approve of such deception? Maquillage works both ways. I see no difference between swamping the new Eucharist with traditional music and swamping the old Mass in vernacular hymns. In either case it is an exercise in hypocrisy.

4. "In any case the present rite is not laid down to be unchanged for eternity." Indeed not: it has already spawned three forms for kiddies and two for reconciliation—and there are plenty more to come when the present lull is over. In Birkenhead they will all be said in Latin, will they? Nonsense, Charles, and you know it.

   While on this topic, I have two remarks to make.

   a) Why is it that those who defend the New Ordo (like your good self in your present mood), why is it that you never mention the rites for kiddies and reconcillies? You always talk as though the N.O. were a stable entity whereas it is a movement—as is proven by the said rites for kiddies and reconcillies. Is that why you do not mention them, because the fact is unpalatable? The choice, therefore, is not between the Old and the New Order but between the Old Order and the New Movement. The language is secondary, provided movement is maintained.

   b) Have we any indication as to how this Movement will evolve? We have, Charles, and you know it. From Cardinal Suenens down to disgruntled curates in Birkenhead and Stamford we see the movement following an identical course: towards charismatism. Were it not so terrifying it would be frightfully funny. Having got rid of the old Mass which the priest said in Latin, we are heading for a charismatic seance in which the laity glossolalize in Hebrew.

5. "Where I agree with you is that the vernacular has failed." Good—and thank God for that! Your basic reason for saying so also seems to me sound: "the same set of words is unsuitable for people with different educational backgrounds even in England, let alone throughout the English-speaking world." True. But has it never struck you that the translations were made into "vernacular" precisely to avoid the religious overtones of the great languages of Christendom? It is the same in France, Germany, Italy, Spain; the translations are into "vernacular," not into French, German, Italian or Spanish. All our languages were formed in the Ages of Faith and bear the indelible marks thereof. A new, faithless language must be used: vernacular, pidgin or "business" English, "*petit-nègre*" in French, and so on. The reason? Because you cannot express the doctrines of the Faith in vernacular, whereas you cannot help expressing them in the languages of Christendom. That is why Cranmer's Communion Service sounds so much more Catholic than our vernacular Mass: it uses a Christian language and we do not.

     Thus, when you say that "we agree that the vernacular has failed," I am by no means certain that we do so for the same reasons. You appear to be looking at the problem of language itself. I am looking at the doctrines which the language cannot convey. To you it is merely the lauguage which has failed. To me the language has succeeded, as was intended in not conveying the truth. Its success is the cause of its failure: the humblest Catholic knows that it is a lie.

There, my dear Charles, are a few reasons why I will have nothing to do with your N.O. in Latin. It might, as you suggest, save my face but it would not save my Faith.

I shall, however, say one thing in favour of the N.O. in Latin, maquillaged with plain-chant. It will make life more tolerable for countless members of your flock. I can also see why any priest who loved his people should give it to them. In fact they ought to do so with or without your blessing;

after all, it is perfectly licit. What I fail to understand is that you, the Bishop, should palm off a substitute when you can give your flock the reality. A lie may save a lot of trouble but a lie it remains.

Have you completely dropped the idea of using the Indult? If so, why? Is it that Testa assured you that it is going to be suppressed? Do be an angel and let me know.

◇   ◇   ◇

The above letter appears to have caused deep offence to Bishop Blythe. At least, there is no further correspondence in Bishop Forester's files. I later made inquiries in the diocese of Birkenhead as to whether an Ad clerum *or pastoral letter had been issued requiring or encouraging the use of the New Ordo in Latin. The answer was in the negative.*

23.   Second letter to Philip Goodman, Bishop of Hull.
(The first is #4.)
Tuesday, January 25th, 1977.

Dear Philip,

Thank you for your inquiry. I look forward to nursing my little cancer for quite a long time. It would be a pity to kill it too soon.

So you have changed your mind—or my little cancer has done it for you. You admit that I have a right to what I have done but its immediate "divisiveness" outweighs any possible benefits. "Divisiveness" is among Testastorta's favourite words. I hope you did not pick it up from him?

"Divisiveness"—it is a funny word. I doubt if it is English. I take it to mean: "a state or condition (=ness) having the nature or capacity (=ive) to divide." So the fact that I have called a halt in my own diocese to the process of auto-demolition in the Church is "state having the nature to divide." Of course it has: from auto-demolition, from suicide. But that is not quite what you mean.

You mean two distinct things: 1. My action puts me out of step with you and my other episcopal brethren; 2. I am not following the post-conciliar orientation. The first is a question of drill: I am out of step. The second is a question of direction: where the regiment is going.

Now, it must surely be admitted by one and all that up to the death of Pius XII the drill was so perfect as to be worthy of Martinet himself and the direction along the straight and narrow path so certain that one could go with one's eyes shut. Those indeed were the criticisms: martinetism and the faith of a sleep-walker. And from whom did these criticisms come? They did not come from the rank and file, who were delighted to be in step and certain of their destination. They came from the officers, who thought of themselves as above the common herd. As to the second criticism (the religion of sleep-walkers), it came from "thinking Catholics," that is the *periti* and their clients; as to the first (Papal martinetism), it came from us, the bishops. It was the unholy alliance of bishops and experts which induced a weak C.O. (always keen to please) to issue the orders: "Break ranks and scatter." The troops, inured to discipline, promptly did so. That is where the division lies and how it came about. You accuse me of being divisive because I am trying to round up my company again and put it back on the straight and narrow with a minimal semblance of drill. I am divisive in the sense that order is divisive of chaos.

You know that this is true from your own personal experience. Take your first point: I am out of step with my episcopal colleagues. Are they in step? We both attend the National Episcopal Conference. Have you noticed a single important issue on which we agree? Catechetics, schools, training colleges; ecumenism, *communicatio in sacris*; the priesthood, its nature, its celibacy; diocesan parochial and extra-parochial structures, etc ... why, even Canon Law, morals and dogma: tell me one on which we are solidly agreed and have a firm, intelligible policy. All we do is huddle together to keep warm and issue a statement to paper over the cracks. You then accuse me of being divisive because my action reveals the division.

It is exactly the same with your second point: that I am not following the post-conciliar orientation. Tell me plainly and honestly what that "orientation" is. You have not a clue. All you know is that it permits any path other than the straight and narrow. I admit, however, that the "post-conciliar orientation" does indicate something: which way the

80

wind is blowing. It is a weathercock. Again you accuse me of being divisive because my action tends to reunite the existing division by giving back to the troops a stable, certain destination.

There is another point I wish to make concerning "divisiveness." The order "to break ranks and scatter" was given by the C.O. (the Pope) at the request of the officers, both commissioned (the bishops) and non-commissioned (the *periti*). This has been the fundamental act of "divisiveness": it has divided the officers from the rank and file. The officers, along with a few batmen and NAAFI nuns, are sitting comfortably by the fire in the nearest pub quaffing pints of beer and endlessly dialoguing as to what next to do. In the meantime the troops are out in the storm. Half have already deserted, some are getting mutinous and the rest are restless. That is the great divide. It is you, not I, who are being "divisive" and the division lies between you and your rankers, the wretched laity. Then you accuse me of being "divisive" because I leave your company in the pub to round up my company, the faithful committed to my care. We bishops should ponder that terrible remark ascribed to Napoleon: "There is no such thing as a bad soldier; there are only bad officers."

Lastly, I do not think it will be difficult to round up the regiment and get it moving again along the straight and narrow. We may even pick up a fair number of the deserters. But they will have got out of the habit of drill. It will take some time to restore it. For the moment we shall have to be satisfied with harmony in the direction rather than unity in drill. That is why I have left considerable latitude in my *Ad clerum*.

There, my dear Philip, at last I have finished. I hope and pray that you will stop talking about "divisiveness" and do something to restore harmony.

◊   ◊   ◊

24.   Second letter to Stephen O'Keary, Bishop of Devizes.
    (The first is #5.)
Monday, January 24th, 1977.

Dear Stephen,

So you have found the explanation for my otherwise incomprehensible action: at the approach of death the mind automatically reverts to the strong impressions of youth. I am motivated by sentiment and nostalgia, quite understandably in view of my condition. You have successfully identified the why and wherefore of my folly.

But I wonder if you are right. The trouble seems to me that we have totally different values. Just as you regard tradition with scorn whereas I hold it in deepest reverence, so is it with sentiment—and this quite apart from my imminent demise. In fact what most annoys me about the accusations made against traditionalists is that we are dubbed "mere sentimentalists."

What a wonderful thing is sensibility, the capacity of man to feel. And this capacity goes far deeper than sensation, experience. Man can stretch his personality into the object he senses so that he touches its reality. And this reality reflects back into him and produces an astonishing reaction, the sentiment, which at its highest level we call love. Only this morning after Mass I watched with ineffable awe as the sun rose; I stretched out towards it and it permeated me: I loved it. Feeling, sensibility, sentiment, love—they are part of what is sublime in our make-up. Of course I am sentimental; at least I try to be. I find it difficult because by nature I am rather impatient and harsh, although not ungrateful. But I have to push myself out quite deliberately into other beings and things in order to touch their reality and so love them instead of merely experiencing the sensation of their existence.

Tell me, Stephen, are you unfeeling? Can't you love? Nonsense! You are as soppy a man as I know. That is what makes you so attractive. You are only a bore when you start being intellectual. From Doctor O'Keary, the Great Theologian, O Lord deliver us!

Now it so happens that a great many Catholics loved the Mass. As they knelt in their pews, apparently indifferent, their whole personality was stretched to its ultimate limit and touched the underlying reality of the Sacrifice of God Incarnate. There was a click, a hiccup, a flame—I don't know what to call it—and they adored. They were in love. Passions change but love does not. They were in love forever. No Pope, bishop or priest can alter it.

"You are being sentimental, Edmund." Exactly, Stephen; and it is the sentiment, not the intellectual formula, which is the reflection of the reality.

And don't start arguing that we can get our click or hiccup just as easily from the New Rite as from the Old. We cannot. On the Divine side the sacrifice is doubtless the same but not on the human. Access to Calvary has been forbidden. Trespassers are prosecuted. Over a microphone the guide explains something to tourists. We sit down and weep.

It is then that nostalgia arises. Nostalgia, homesickness, is merely the acute memory of past sentiment. It, too, is a beautiful thing, a God-given grace. I am encouraged to love now from my memory of love past. Even nostalgia of bitter memories is useful; it helps to keep us humble and make us sweeter now.

That is the trouble with revolutionaries; they have no sentiments and no nostalgia. They do not love anything and never have. That is why they build an imaginary love into the future, because they know it never comes. Also they are incapable of understanding that other people do love and have loved, that the simplest souls are capable of the highest sentiments. Therein, indeed, lies the only equality among mortals.

How can anyone dare stamp on other people's sentiments? Who has given them permission? "The hankering after the Old Mass is pure sentimentality." Of course it is, and that is precisely why it is sacrosanct.

You also say that "sentimentality and nostalgia lead automatically to superstition." I doubt it. However, I shall spare you my comments on their interconnections. But I do want to defend superstition. It is at worst silly. It implies believing more than the evidence warrants: 13, ladders, magpies and the like—ridiculous but not wicked. When it comes to religion, it may still be ridiculous but is still not wicked. In religion, in fact, it at least indicates the presence of a virtue: the willingness to believe. It shows a generous disposition. Now, what we suffer from today is not superstition at all but infrastition: believing far less than the evidence warrants. This is the cancer of the revolutionaries and it is infinitely more malignant than mine. But what I really hold against infrastition is that it is mean. Fancy being mean to God!

I am supposed to be near death, so you must allow me the privilege of saying what otherwise would seem impertinent: be sentimental, be loving and don't be mean.

◊　◊　◊

Bishop Forester's letters to his other episcopal colleagues are without significance, mere covering notes to the printed slip concerning his health. There is evidence that he received an important letter from Archbishop Weir of Derby but, if he answered it, he did so in longhand and there is no copy. He did, however, address a long letter to Mr Solly Glauben.

25.   To Mr. Solly Glauben,
            Glauben House, London, SWI.
Tuesday, January 25th, 1977.

Dear Mr. Glauben,
    Rarely if ever have I read a letter which moved me more than yours. I shall answer it anon and get rid of business first.
    Last week my secretary acknowledged your incredibly generous gift. I did not reply immediately because it is clear that a Trust will have to be established to administer the funds received, which now amount to nearly £30,000. This money belongs neither to me nor to the diocese of Stamford. Before writing to you I wanted to make sure that the Dowager Duchess of Blackwater would act as chairman and that Sir John Cutting (the well-known Judge) would be one of the Trustees. Both have consented, as has a certain Mr. Christopher Outman, chairman of Stamfordshire County Council. I am thinking in terms of eight trustees of whom three would be clergy, including myself. Now, it seems to me that you ought to be one of the five laymen. The trouble is that you know none of us and none of us knows you. Besides, you are likely to be far too occupied to devote time and attention to a trifling Trust in Stamfordshire. However, at 6 p.m. on Thursday next, February 3rd, at the invitation of Selina Duchess of Blackwater, The Old Hall, Blackwater, SD7 5QR, there will be a preliminary meeting of the proposed Trustees along with the Duchess's solicitors, to instruct the latter in drawing up the Trust Deed. The time and date cannot be altered because of Sir John's engagements. Naturally, we shall dine at the Old Hall and, if you do not wish to drive back to London that night, the Duchess will be delighted to put you up.
    (There follow detailed instructions on how to get to Blackwater.)

84

So much for business. Now to your letter. As I have said, I was deeply moved by it. Perhaps what struck me most was your remark:

"I am a convert to the Sacrificial Presence of God Incarnate in the Mass."

Now, if you join the Trust, you will find that out of eight members three are converts. It is a high percentage. The three of you come from totally different religious backgrounds. All three of you are converts to the Real Presence under one aspect or another.

1. There is yourself, the faithful member of the Chosen People, who has had nothing to deny but has found the apotheosis of all he believes in the Sacrificial Presence of God Incarnate: God's ultimate faithfulness beyond which it is impossible to go.

2. The Duchess. As you will see if you come on Thursday, she is a very matter-of-fact, down-to-earth sort of woman. Her background was practicing Anglican. She has told me several times: "Of course God is a hidden God. Who can conceivably see God and live? That is why He makes us die. But at least Catholics know where He hides. That is why I became one: to know the hiding-hole of the Hidden God."

3. My friend Father Bryan Houghton. You will not meet him on Thursday because he lives in the South of France. His background is one of liberal agnosticism. This is his approach. "The Real Presence is the physical evidence of Deicide, the killing of God, the ultimate in crime. It is turned into the guarantee of the criminals' salvation, the ultimate in God's omnipotence and mercy. The true religion is of necessity the religion of ultimates. If not, what is beyond would be true."

In the odd twenty years that I had cure of souls, either as curate or parish priest, I doubt if I ever received fewer than ten converts a year into the Church. I loved them. Along with the Eternal Truths I gave them all I had to offer. I never talked down to them, no matter how simple they were. The human mind can absorb infinitely more than it can rationalize and explain. How wonderful they were and how I admired them! Even if I knew that they lacked the discipline and willpower to practice as they should, I knew also that they were making a pathetic, disinterested gesture towards God, the beauty of which would never tarnish. Nobility and gentry, drunks and tramps, I have received them all.

I suppose rather over half, say 60%, were "marriage converts." They were often among the best. Human love seems a natural introduction to divine love. In those days, the Catholic knew he had something to give and the non-Catholic something to receive. It was right and proper that the wedding ring should be set with the Pearl of Great Price. And the heroism of so many of those marriage converts! Not only were they cut off by their families (a more tragic situation in the working than in the educated classes), but they undertook willingly to obey the marriage laws. "I am only a marriage convert, Father"; my dear, you could be nothing more noble.

About half of the remainder, being English, were far too inarticulate to give any reason for their conversion. I could fill pages on these extraordinary people. It was an event in their lives as inexplicable as their existence: a pure intervention of grace. Who is to jeer at that?

Of those who could explain their attraction if not their conversion to the Church, the largest group connected it with the Real Presence—very remotely, of course, because they knew nothing about it; but that was the reason. I explain: "I went into one of your churches out of the rain. Nobody was there. I wandered round. There was an oil lamp hanging from the ceiling. It wasn't doing anything, not lighting or heating, just hanging and flickering. I thought: 'It's just like me, hanging about and flickering round.' Then I felt somebody was there. I looked about and there wasn't. But there was etc. . . ." The bells at the elevation during Mass have awakened countless souls. In fact, the only thing which, in my experience, has never converted anybody is a sermon. Things do; words don't.

I noticed three other groups: the quest for certitude, particularly among practicing Anglicans; the longing for forgiveness of sin, fairly common among the highly refined; an urge for devotion to Our Lady, noticeable among devout Nonconformists but also among the very simple.

Where do they stand now, all my wonderful converts? I fear, Mr Glauben, that your terrible verdict does not only apply to the priest who received you. I too, unwittingly, "deceived them into the Church." May God forgive me. And may I spend what little life remains to me in making reparation.

◇　◇　◇

On Tuesday, January 25th, the clergy of Stamford diocese received Bishop Forester's Ad clerum *in answer to the Catholic press. On Wednesday they received an anonymous circular purporting to come from "A Canon Lawyer." Its message was simple: Bishop Forester had no right to permit the Tridentine Mass in his diocese because it was forbidden by Rome. The author produced the usual quotations from the* Constitutio *of April 3rd, 1969, the two Notifications of June 14th, 1971 and October 28th, 1974 and the Holy Father's Consistorial Allocution of May 24th, 1976.*

The reason why Bishop Forester wrote no significant letters on Wednesday and Thursday of this week is doubtless due to his being occupied in answering this circular.

26.　　To the Clergy of Stamford Diocese.
Ad clerum 77-3
Monday, January 31st, 1977.

Right Reverend, Very Reverend and Reverend Fathers,

I apologize for bombarding you with circulars. Doubtless I started it but I am not solely responsible for its continuation.

You received an anonymous and undated circular on Wednesday which purported to prove that I had no right to permit the Immemorial Mass in this diocese. This, you are well aware, is nonsense, as can be seen from the general law of the Church, article 22 of Constitution of November 1963, article 6 of the General Instructions to the New Ordo of 1969, etc. . . . and by common sense, all of which commit the liturgy to the pastoral care of the chief pastor, the bishop, so long as he is acting within the General Law of the Church.

The circular, however, gives me the opportunity of going

87

into the question of the licitness of the Immemorial Mass in some detail. It has all been said before by Professors Louis Salleron and Neri Capponi and by Father Bryan Houghton among others, but it is more than likely that your attention has not been drawn to their publications and, if it has, you have not had time to read them. As you will see, I am attempting to do much more than answer the circular. I am trying to guide you through the labyrinth of documents in which the Mass has been lost, so that you will know how you stand in the event of my death.

I. THE SITUATION BEFORE VATICAN II

It should be remembered that until 1570 no Pope and no Council had ever legislated over the rite in which Mass was celebrated. The astonishing similarity between the rites in the Western Church arose from the fact that no bishop or priest dared innovate in anything so sacred. If in doubt, they discovered what was the common practice in Rome. The attitude was notably different from that of some contemporary priests who seem to imagine that the Eucharist would be invalid if they failed to tinker with it. Actually, the only attempt to unify the rite came from civil, not ecclesiastical authority. After the conquest of Old Saxony, completed in A.D. 775, Charlemagne was faced with the problem of its evangelization. To facilitate and integrate the missioners' work he instructed the Anglo-Saxon, Alcuin of York, to unify the rites current in the Empire.

It was the Protestant reformers who first dared to touch the rite of the Sacred Mysteries. Eucharistic forms multiplied with the same rapidity that they do today. It was to restore order in the existing chaos that the Council of Trent called upon the Pope to establish a norm for the celebration of Mass. Hence the first Papal legislation on the subject, the Bull *Quo Primum* of St Pius V of July 19th, 1570. What did this Bull do?

1. It consolidated and codified (*statuimus et ordinamus* are the operative words) the Immemorial Roman Rite.

2. It made its use compulsory throughout the Latin Church, except

3. when other rites had a continuous usage of over two hundred years, such as those of Sarum, Lyons, Toledo, Milan, the Dominicans, the Carthusians, etc.

4. It granted a perpetual Indult to all priests under any circumstances to celebrate according to the Immemorial Roman Rite thus codified.

It is to be observed, therefore, that the so-called "Tridentine Rite" does not exist by the positive law of one Pope which the next is at liberty to undo. It exists by immemorial custom to which the laity who attend it have as much right as the clergy who celebrate it. Is it not possible that this point has been overlooked? Anyway, an immemorial right can be extinguished by two means:

a) by a solemn pronouncement of the Sovereign Pontiff abrogating the customary right on the grounds that its continuance would be contrary to the common good;

b) by the customary right falling into desuetude—along with the custom the right lapses.

On the other hand, what is of positive law in the Bull *Quo Primum* is the exclusivity granted to the Immemorial Roman Rite, apart from rites over two hundred years old. This exclusivity can clearly be modified by a succeeding Pope without any appeal to "reasonableness" and "the common good."

II. THE COUNCIL

Such was the position on which we were all agreed, Pope, bishops, priests, laity, up to and including the Council.

In November 1963 the Council promulgated its Constitution on the liturgy, *Sacrosanctum Concilium*. It should be noted that this document is a Constitution, the most solemn form of legislation of which a Council is capable. What does it do? Does it abrogate (=abolish), obrogate (=substitute) or derogate (=make exceptions to) previous legislation and notably the Bull *Quo Primum*? Not a bit of it; it takes it all for granted. It merely speaks of *instauratio*. The Latin *instaurare* does not mean to restore in the sense of restoring a ruined building. It means to restore in the way we restore our tissues in a restaurant. In fact it means to refresh. Even the refreshment was to be pretty abstemious as we learn from article 36: "The use of the Latin language shall be maintained (*servetur*) in the Latin rites." Article 54 allows for the local dialects "above all for the lessons and community prayers . . . also in the responses of the people." In fact a vernacular dialogued Mass was permitted although not made compulsory. Please re-read *Sacrosanctum Concilium* without hindsight: what it says, not what it has been made to say.

So far we have two laws, both duly promulgated in the most solemn form of which the Church is capable:

1. A Papal Constitution, the Bull *Quo Primum* of 1570;

2. A Conciliar Constitution, *Sacrosanctum Concilium* of 1963. The second confirms the first, merely permitting certain specific derogations in the matter of language by its article 54.

III. THE SEQUENCE

1. Two months later, on January 25th, 1964, Pope Paul VI issued a *motu proprio* called *Sacram Liturgiam*. A *motu proprio* is a binding Papal document, be it legislative, judicial or administrative. What passes belief is that this is the only one on the liturgy which the Pope has issued to date, that is in thirteen years. This unique document fixes the parts of the Mass to be said in the native dialect as recommended by article 54 of *Sacrosanctum Concilium*: the introductory psalm, epistle and gospel, etc. Unfortunately, it also announced the creation of a special Consilium (with an 's' in the middle, consequently an advisory body) to put into effect the Council's recommendations. This was duly established on February 29th under the chairmanship of Cardinal Lercaro.

2. It look a little time for the Consilium to warm to its work and its first publication, the Institution *Inter Oecumenici*

of September 26th, 1964, could, with a bit of pushing and pulling, be fitted into the Council's Constitution. It permitted (but did not enjoin) the whole of the Mass apart from the Preface and Canon to be said in the vernacular. It reintroduced the bidding-prayers, which the Council had never demanded. It also delegated liturgical powers to bishops.

It was from this moment onwards that serious opposition began to be felt. For instance, I think the Latin Mass Society was founded early in 1965. Several perfectly reasonable priests rang the alarm. Myself, being neither a theologian nor a Canon Lawyer but a clerical accountant, thought *Inter Oecumenici* unwise but not impossible. I became your bishop.

3. Owing perhaps to the opposition, the Consilium remained reasonably inactive for nearly three years. Then, on May 4th, 1967 it produced its *Tres Abhinc Annos*, better known as the *Instructio Altera*. This, my dear Fathers, was the revolution. Permission was granted for the whole Mass, including the Canon and Consecration, to be said aloud and in the vernacular. This is clean contrary to paragraphs 1 and 2 of article 36 of *Sacrosanctum Concilium*. It was, of course, a derogation from the law, a pure permission, but we were all made to realize that laws were no longer meant to be obeyed whereas permissions were obligatory.

What is the legal value of such an Instruction? It is not easy to determine. The Consilium, as its name implied was a counselling body. It should therefore have induced either the Pope to issue a *motu proprio* or the Ministry concerned, the Congregation of Rites, to send out a Notification. It did neither but issued its own Instruction. Whatever its value, one thing is quite certain: it cannot derogate from any existing law, in the particular case from the Pope's *motu proprio* of January 25th, 1964 and from the Council's Constitution. It was a try-on.

The trouble is that it worked. Neither the Pope nor the episcopate questioned the *Instructio Altera*. From that moment onwards the progressive bureaucracy knew that it was master. The bishops, from Rome to Stamford, had abdicated.

4. The extent of the abdication became almost immediately evident. In October of the same year, 1967, the Consilium produced its *Missa Normativa* at the Synod of Bishops. It was rejected by 104 votes to 72. What did that matter? It has become law as the New Ordo.

IV. THE NEW ORDO:
A. THE CONSTITUTION *MISSALE ROMANUM*

This has the most puzzling history of all. May I remind you, Fathers, that we already have two documents of the highest conceivable authority: the Bull *Quo Primum* and the Constitution *Sacrosanctum Concilium*, which are, moreover, in line with each other. What happens next?

On April 3rd, 1969, a Papal Constitution entitled *Missale Romanum* was promulgated purporting to be the law governing the New Order of Mass, as yet unpublished. In this original version it is not a law at all but an explanatory introduction to a permission. Even the word *Constitutio* is nowhere to be found in the text, merely in the title. There is no abrogation of previous legislation and no clause ordering the use of the new rite. There is no sentence to show that it is obligatory, let alone exclusive. There is no dating clause to show when it should come into effect.

This, of course, did not prevent the powers that be from saying that it was a binding law. To do so they had recourse to a mistranslation. What is so curious is that this mistranslation was common to all languages. I have read it myself in English, French and Italian; I am told that it is the same in German and Spanish. How can this possibly come about? How can all these expert translators make the identical howler? Your guess is as good as mine.

Here is the sentence, the fourth before the end of the original version, the fifth in the *Acta*:

> Ad extremum, ex iis quae hactenus de novo Missali Romano exposuimus quiddam nunc *cogere et efficere* placet. . . .

I have underlined the mistranslated words. *Cogere et efficere* is a well-known Ciceronian phrase to be found in most dictionaries. Even if the translators could not be bothered to look it up, it is perfectly clear that *quiddam cogere* breaks down into *agere quiddam con* = to work something together, which is in the context "to sum up." Equally, *quiddam efficere* breaks down into *facere quiddam ex* = to make something out, which is in the context "to draw a conclusion." The sentence therefore means: "Lastly, from what we have so far declared concerning the New Roman Missal, we should now like to sum up and draw a conclusion." And what did all the translators make of it? "In conclusion, We now wish to give the force of law to all We have declared . . ."; and in French, "Pour terminer, Nous voulons donner force de loi à tout ce que Nous avons exposé . . ."; and in Italian, etc. . . . It is strange, my dear Fathers, but such is the truth: "to sum up and draw a conclusion" becomes "to give the force of law."

And what did I do about it? Absolutely nothing for the simple reason that I did not bother to read the Latin until two or three years later. Do not judge me too severely. Have you read it?

But that is not the end. Worse is to come. The *Acta* for June 1969 were published as usual about two months later. When it appeared a brand new clause had been inserted into the original document as the penultimate paragraph. It reads: "*Quae Constitutione hac Nostra praescripsimus vigere incipient a XXX proximi mensis Novembris hoc anno, id est a Dominica I Adventus.*" That is: "What We have ordered by this Our Constitution will begin to take effect as from November 30th of this year (1969), that is the First Sunday of Advent." You will notice that for the first and only time the word *Constitutio* appears in the text. For the first time, too, a word signifying "to order" is introduced—*praescripsimus.* For the first time a date is given on which the order is to become effective. Thus is a permission turned into a law.

Actually, there are a couple of snags even about this insertion. The word *praescripsimus*—We have ordered—is not the proper term in Latin, but I shall not bother you with such refinements. More important, it is in the wrong tense. Up to this point the legislator has prescribed nothing at all. It is precisely in this clause that he claims to do so. The verb, therefore, should be in the present tense, *praescribimus*— "what We are ordering by this our Constitution": not in the perfect, "what We have prescribed." The only explanation I can think of for this howler is recognition by its author that he is tampering with a pre-existing text. Moreover, the logical

93

conclusion from the use of the wrong tense can scarcely be what its author intended: since nothing *was* prescribed, nothing *is* prescribed; and the legislator, to boot, is still prescribing nothing. What a mess! I wonder how long a civil government would last which thus tampered with its own laws?

There is a last remark I wish to make about this strange document. It winds up with the usual *clause de style*: "We wish, moreover, that these decisions and ordinances of ours should be stable and effective now and in future, notwithstanding—in so far as may be necessary—Constitutions and Apostolic Regulations published by Our Predecessors and all other ordinances, even those requiring special mention and derogation." At long last—indeed it is the last word—there is a technical term in the Constitution, so we know exactly where we stand: "derogation." The New Ordo is therefore only a permission after all. It is merely a licit exception, a derogation, to the previous laws which are still in force. They have not been abrogated. But surely it is only a mistake? The author of the *praescripsimus* clause forgot to alter the *clause de style*? Maybe, but it proves three things: 1. one's sins always find one out; 2. the author has a highly efficient Guardian Angel; 3. it is nonsense to claim that the Bull *Quo Primum* has been abrogated.

Mistranslation, insertion, error: it is all highly distasteful. Needless to say there has been no apology, explanation or withdrawal. It is those who point out these irregularities who are accused of being disloyal and divisive.

Do these irregularities invalidate the Constitution? Of course not; it is a valid law in the terms published in the *Acta*. At most it could be maintained that the wrong tense of *praescripsimus* makes its meaning doubtful and *lex dubia non obligat*—but it does not much matter as it is only a permission anyway. No, the irregularities do not invalidate the law. All they do is to make me highly suspicious of the present administration.

To sum up:

1. The Constitution *Missale Romanum* of April 3rd, 1969 has been duly promulgated. That is why I permit the use of the New Ordo in this diocese.

2. It has derogated from the exclusive use of the Immemo-

rial Mass but has not abrogated the Bull *Quo Primum*. That is why I permit the use of the Tridentine Rite.

3. It has not abrogated the Conciliar Constitution *Sacrosanctum Concilium*. That is why I permit: a) the "hybrid" Mass; b) the reintroduction of the Offertory etc. into the New Ordo—since these are in line with the said Constitution.

B. THE *INSTITUTIO GENERALIS* AND THE NEW *PRECES*.

1. One of the reasons why the all-important Constitution received such scant attention was that on April 6th (consequently two months before its publication in the *Acta*) the New Mass forms were released, preceded by a theologico-rubrical introduction called the *Institutio Generalis*. I am ashamed to say that it was received with unctuous enthusiasm by us bishops, although the Mass rites were practically identical with what our synod had rejected in October 1967. You priests were marginally better; you received it with glum gloom but little protest. Opposition was left to the laity. It became highly vociferous and found expression in the Critical Study presented by Cardinals Ottaviani and Bacci to the Pope on September 25th of the same year. If you have kept a copy of the Critical Study, please re-read it. You will notice that it does not merely criticize the theology of the introduction but the Mass rites which give expression to that theology.

2. This opposition did in fact have some effect. On October 20th, less than a month after the Critical Study had been presented to the Pope, the Consilium issued an Instruction, *Constitutione Apostolica*, delaying the introduction of the New Ordo from November 30th, 1969 to November 28th, 1971, nominally to give time to prepare vernacular translations. In the meantime the New Ordo could be said in Latin. On the other hand, in this document also we hear for the first time that the Immemorial Mass may only be said by aged priests *sine populo*, without a congregation. This is pure usurpation of power and has no basis in law.

95

3. On the following March 26th, 1970, a new edition of the *Institutio Generalis* was issued. The heretical clause 7— "The Mass is the sacred synaxis or congregation of the People of God"—was made merely ambiguous and clauses 48, 55, 56 and 60 were amended. So much for the permanent value of the most solemn Roman documents under the present administration. Not only is there tampering with the basic law governing the New Ordo, but its theological justification has to be amended within a year of publication. This certainly calls for blind obedience since it is difficult to obey with eyes open. What remains quite inexplicable, however, is that the Mass forms themselves have not been changed. Their theological justification has gone; they are unaltered.

Incidentally, it is in that same year, the year of opposition, that the English Martyrs were canonized and Cardinal Heenan of blessed memory secured his Indult.

V. THE NEW ORDO IN OPERATION

1. As I have said, the opposition was almost exclusively lay. The powers that be could not deal with it as summarily as they could with the clergy. There was over a year of patient waiting to see if the laity could organize themselves. It became clear that with an inadequate supply of priests and no bishop they could not. Hence we got the second revolutionary document. You will remember that the first was the *Instructio Altera* of May 4th, 1967, which decided, contrary to the law, that the whole of the Mass, including the consecration, should be said aloud and in the vernacular. Well, this time it is a bit worse. On June 14th, 1971 the Congregation for Worship issued a Notification granting to Episcopal Conferences the right to impose the exclusive use of the vernacular in the New Ordo, once the translations had been approved. It thus became illicit to celebrate the New Ordo in Latin. So much for the Constitution *Sacrosanctum Concilium*. It also repeated the provision in the Instruction of October 20th, 1969 that the Old Mass could only be said by aged priests *sine populo*.

Be it noted that a Notification is a purely administrative document and has no legislative authority whatsoever. Moreover, this particular one was itself undated and unsigned. It is therefore worth less than the paper on which it was printed. The bishops, from Rome to Stamford, remained mute.

2. Of course, the inevitable result of this particular piece of administrative folly was to throw all Latinists into the arms of the Tridentiners. There was no alternative if the New Ordo was illicit in Latin. It became imperative to divide the opposition, especially as Archbishop Lefebvre had cropped up in the meantime. The laity had thus found a bishop with the promise of future priests. Hence the Notification of October 28th, 1974. This document reverses the previous ruling: the New Ordo may now be said in Latin or vernacular with equality of esteem. The New Ordo, however, is obligatory "notwithstanding the pretext of any custom whatsoever even immemorial." The importance of this last remark is that for the first time the establishment admitted the existence of immemorial rights, even if only to brush them aside.

3. From this moment onwards the assault against the old rite slightly changed tack. At the beginning of this *Ad clerum* I wrote: "An immemorial right can be extinguished by two means:

    a) by a solemn pronouncement of the Sovereign Pontiff abrogating the customary right on the grounds that its continuance would be contrary to the common good;

    b) by the customary right falling into desuetude—along with the custom the right lapses."

It would not be easy to prove that the Immemorial Mass had been contrary to the common good. Who would believe it? Moreover, by 1974 it was a bit late to start saying so, especially as the Council had said nothing of the sort. The alternative was to crush the custom as rapidly as possible, preferably under the existing administration.

This explains the extraordinary animosity against Archbishop Lefebvre: he is busy perpetuating the immemorial custom. It also explains the astonishing pressure brought to bear on the English hierarchy to petition for the withdrawal of Heenan's Indult. In its humble way, the Indult too is preserving the custom. I may add that, if it still exists, it is thanks to Heenan's successor.

4. Great tragedies are heightened by farcical interludes. Four days after the Notification of October 28th, on November 1st, 1974 the Congregation promulgated its two little Eucharists for Reconciliations and three for kiddies.

VI. PAPAL INTERVENTION

You may well ask, in this plethora of Constitutions, Institutions, Instructions and Notifications, has the Pope done or said nothing? The two questions are rather different. What he has done is restricted to: a) the *motu proprio, Sacram Liturgiam*, of January 25th, 1964, which in practice was rendered nugatory by the Consilium's *Instructio Altera*; b) the Constitution, *Missale Romanum*, of April 3rd, 1969, presumably along with the clause inserted into the *Acta*. What he has said is a very different matter. In 1969 there is the Allocution of April 28th, of November 19th, and again of November 26th. As the years roll by, so do the Allocutions. However, they are all summed up in the Consistorial Allocutions of May 24th, 1976 to which the anonymous Canon Lawyer refers. It is a little more harsh than the rest because it was directed against Archbishop Lefebvre. I translate the relevant passage.

It is in the name of tradition itself that We require all our sons and all Catholic communities to celebrate the liturgy according to the renewed rite with dignity and fervour. The use of the New Ordo is by no means left to the discretion of priests and faithful. The Instruction of June 14th, 1971 has provided that the celebration of Mass according to the Old Rite should only be allowed, with the permission of the Ordinary, to aged and sick priests when celebrating with nobody present. The New Ordo has been promulgated to replace the Old after mature deliberation and in order to fulfil the Council's decisions. It is in exactly the same way that Our predecessor St Pius V made obligatory the Missal recognized by his authority after the Council of Trent. By the same supreme authority, which We have received from Christ, We decree the same prompt obedience to all the other reforms, be they liturgical, disciplinary or pastoral, which in recent years have grown up out of the decrees of the Council.

And what is one to say to that?

Well, in the first place the translators have been at it again. In the passage concerning Pius V the Latin has: ". . . St Pius V made obligatory the Missal recognized (*recognitum*) by his authority"—which is perfectly correct; whereas the Italian has ". . . reformed (*riformato*) by his authority"— which is perfectly incorrect but suits the argument better. The whole point is that Pius V reformed nothing at all: he codified the Immemorial Rite; whereas a little later in the same passage Paul VI admits that "the New Ordo has been promulgated to replace the Old." So the New Ordo is not even a reform but a "replacement" or substitution—for which the technical term is obrogation. But not even a Pope can obrogate an immemorial custom—unless there are two or more immemorial customs running concurrently and one is substituted for the other. A new usage cannot obrogate an immemorial custom unless the latter is first abrogated, abolished; only then can the new usage fill the void. Therein, I think, lies the real importance of the text: the admission that the New Ordo is not a reform of the Mass but a substitute for the Mass. Anyway, the statement is nonsense: Pius V did not make the old Ordo exclusive since he allowed all rites over two hundred years old to continue. Neither has Paul VI made the New exclusive since only eighteen months previously he had permitted the rites for Reconciliations and kiddies.

I suppose I should mention briefly a few other points. A Consistorial Allocution is a speech. It is not a law. In the present case it illustrates Paul VI's deep affection for the New Ordo. This is perfectly natural: most parents believe that they beget nothing but swans. More significant is that His Holiness should make no appeal to the only laws on the subject which have been duly promulgated: his own Constitution of 1969 and the Council's of 1963. Concerning the latter he uses a euphemism: "the reforms . . . which in recent years have grown up out of the decrees of the Council." But one has every right to question a "growth" which, in his own words, is a "substitution." His Holiness is therefore led to appeal to what he calls the "Instruction" of June 14th, 1971. This is most unfortunate. As we have seen, the document issued on that date was a mere Notification, itself undated and unsigned. Its legal value is nil. It does, however, contain the gratuitously cruel clause that aged and infirm priests may (with permission, of course) say the Immemorial Mass provided nobody is present. This His Holiness does not blush to repeat. Lastly, the emotional appeal of the passage consists in calling upon the faithful to discard the tradition of worship in the name of the tradition of obedience. Does His Holiness not realize that the tradition of obedience is even more delicate than that of worship? He complains bitterly that he is no longer obeyed. No wonder: tradition as such having been undermined, the tradition of obedience has vanished. It is all terribly sad.

VII. THE PROOF OF PUDDING

At this point, Fathers, I can well imagine you saying: "The old Bishop naturally makes out a good case in his own cause. But how can I tell that his opponents could not do as much? I certainly have not time to verify the documents he mentions, let alone the ones he does not. It is beyond me. I shall just obey, even if I am called a weathercock."

Well, I think you can judge the truth of my contention from the least expected of sources: the Lefebvre affair.

Everyone knows that the real trouble with Archbishop Lefebvre is that he sticks to the Immemorial Mass and is training priests to do the like. Agreed? Of course.

Then, why is it that he was not suspended for that? Wasn't he? No, he was not.

A devious way was found. He is not a diocesan bishop and consequently has no title, no right, to ordain priests. To get round this difficulty he founded the Priestly Confraternity of St Pius X as a diocesan congregation in the diocese of Fribourg. Thus, as bishop-superior of his congregation he could ordain his own subjects. Rome then suppressed his congregation (legally or illegally is beside the point), so that he no longer had the right to ordain. He did ordain. He was suspended.

You see the point? It is precisely because Archbishop Lefebvre could not be suspended for saying the Immemorial Mass that a devious means had to be employed. The Establishment is determined to crush the Old Mass: it cannot do it straight so it will do it crooked.

VIII. TO SUM UP AND CONCLUDE

Nunc quiddam cogere et efficere placet.
A. The summing up

1. You will have noticed that in all the documents I have quoted it is taken for granted that the Mass is the private property of priests. It is not. The priest is the executor of the Testament of God Incarnate but the faithful are just as much beneficiaries under the will as he. It is they, the faithful, who have the right to the Immemorial Mass. They can demand that the Legacy be paid in a currency which has held its value from time immemorial. They are aware that we live in an age of inflation and bright new notes are soon devalued.

2. The Immemorial Mass has not been abrogated—even if it could be. Its use is therefore licit as well as valid.

3. The attack against it is devious: to suppress the custom thanks to the abject conformism of bishops and the servile obedience of priests.

B. Conclusion

1. What I ask of you is to maintain the custom of the Immemorial Mass. You need not say it exclusively so long as you say it sometimes—always mindful, however, that the faithful have a right to it.

2. This would not require much heroism but a little organization might help. The diocese would be unmanageable if about twenty priests were excluded from the ministry. If rather more, say thirty priests, were willing to join a Secular Institute of which one of the objects were the maintenance of the Immemorial Rite, nothing much could be done against you.

101

3. Our Administrator, Mgr Defew, has accepted to found such an Institute. I cannot sufficiently express my gratitude to him. I enclose a form which you will kindly return to him if you are willing to join the Institute.

4. If fewer than thirty diocesan priests have joined the Institute by April 1st, the project will be abandoned and I shall rely on the courage and integrity of individual priests to preserve the custom of the Mass of Ages.

I have written this *Ad clerum* on Wednesday and Thursday, January 26/7th. I shall not post it, however, until I have decided whether or not to reopen the diocesan seminary. If I find this practical it is clear that the Institute will be heavily reinforced.

P.S. Monday, January 31st. I have decided to reopen the diocesan seminary. The Rector will be Mgr Charles Bouverie, ex-Vice-Rector of the English College. The five existing students are willing to attend it. Mgr Bouverie and I have accepted five applicants for the Summer Term and a further six for September. The new students understand that their acceptance for the diocese is conditional on their joining Mgr Defew's Secular Institute.

The only other substantial letter written by Bishop Forester during the week was that to the Mother Provincial of the Veronican Sisters in connection with the Sludge affair on Friday, January 28th. It has already appeared as Letter 14.

CHAPTER IV

HOPE

27.   To the Reverend Bryan Houghton,
          Avignon, France.
Sunday, January 30th, 1977.

Dear Bryan,

When I wrote to you last week I was about as depressed as I can be—which is fortunately not very much. It seemed to me grossly unfair to reveal my cancer to all the world. However, on balance it has probably done my cause more good than harm. The bishops, of course, have all cried off, including Blythe. Their main interest is who will succeed me as member of the Club. I bet the auxiliaries are polishing their rosaries and licking Testa's toes. Incidentally, I have not heard from him nor from the Delegate who is still in Rome. The only really sympathetic letter I received, both compassionate and encouraging, came from that strange fellow Weir of Derby. He must have been ashamed of such sentimentality because he asked me to burn it. Also the Cardinal sent me a postcard: "My admiration for your courage has been heightened by the knowledge of your condition"—just that, unsigned.

But Defew (the Administrator) tells me that it has produced an astonishing reaction in my favour among the clergy.

According to him, my first *Ad clerum* had puzzled and upset them; they were uncertain what to do. The attack on me immediately brought out their sense of fair play. I wrote them a second, rather pathetic little *Ad clerum*; it was perfectly sincere because I was depressed. Apparently it put the lid on their reaction: the poor old Bish needs protection! I do, of course; and I am grateful for it.

Then on Wednesday they got a circular to say that I had no right to permit the old Mass. It was neither new nor profound. I enclose my answer. It is frightfully boring but it needs saying and not one bishop in the world has said it—and you are one of the very few priests who has.

As for the laity, the reaction has been simply staggering. People love a sob story anyway and to discover that the hero is a victim and victimized is too good to be true. I could not help comparing the reaction of my colleagues to that of humble folk: the one so calculating and hard, the other so sentimental and generous. Talking of generosity, the money still comes rolling in. In fact it has started coming from Australia and the States. Miss Defew has banked over £50,000.

(There follow details about the first meeting of the Trust to be held on the following Thursday, February 3rd.)

On Friday morning Socks returned to Sandborough. Largely thanks to him everything is running quite smoothly here. His parish needs him more than I. He has been absolutely wonderful. Without him it would have taken me a week to write the enclosed *Ad clerum*. He laid his finger immediately on all the relevant documents. I wish they would appoint him my successor. I know he is not a traditionalist—he is too cynical to be anything—but at least he would see that there was fair play. The trouble is that he has been far too closely associated with me.

Bouverie arrived for lunch, just after Socks had left. I had met him a couple of times previously but this time he has impressed me far more. The treatment he has received has built up in him enormous reserves of strength. We spent the afternoon discussing the Idea of a Seminary: he has all the right ones. Also, he had worked it out in great detail: the minimum intake to be viable (six); the ratio of staff to students; the actual courses; the qualifications of the staff; running costs, etc. What is more, he can lay his hand on the staff as he has kept in touch with a number of sound and disillu-sioned professors.

Yesterday and today we have been interviewing the can-didates who seemed most likely on paper: all eleven ex-sem-inarians (a new one had applied) and another nine aged 18 to 21. It was a gruelling task for Bouverie but he is brilliant at it. Defew and myself just listened in.

The stories from the seminarians were utterly pathetic: the jeers and sneers at the piety which they had brought with them from home; the discrediting of "bourgeois culture," which included objective morality, the substitution of doing good for being good, of experience for revelation, of human-ism for the Divine, of questions where there should be an-swers, evolving theology instead of dogma—and the lot with-out any philosophical background, ascetic discipline or training in prayer. In fact there was little common ground between the ideals of their vocation and the ideas at the sem-inary. Bouverie extracted it all as easily as turning on a tap.

And all those dear boys had wanted to serve God at His altar, stand innocent in His presence and reconcile the world to Him, just as I had fifty years ago (and, by His grace, still do). But no matter how noble and innocent they may have been, six of them were of little use now. Their experience had left a scar which even their obvious good will could not ef-face: in one scruples, in another doubt, in a third bitterness and so on. And Bryan, one of those whom we rejected had been a student for the diocese of Stamford. I am responsible before God for the failure of his vocation. This, you know, is a frightful thought. There in front of me was a young man whose vocation I had destroyed and whom I was unwilling to take back. Thank God that in His infinite mercy He has sent me a minute penance, my silly little cancer. How I must love and cherish it if in any conceivable way it can repair the harm I have done.

Anyway, we have accepted five of them. They have all done between two and four years at a Senior Seminary or its equivalent. At the moment their ages range between 22 and 27. We have not promised them a date for ordination or whether their previous years will count. Bouverie was quite firm on that score: "You may have so much to unlearn." They are to start after Easter; they can all give up their jobs. Bou-verie has planned a special course for them as for our existing students. Two of them are quite first class; the remaining three will require some attention.

Of the nine between 18 and 21 we have accepted six for September. Three were quite obviously enthusiasts whose flame was likely to burn out.

Next weekend and the one after we shall interview as many more, since applications are still coming in. The trouble, of course, is that Stamford cannot normally absorb more than four ordinations a year. Bouverie requires a minimum of six. At the moment we can take all six owing to the drop in vocations since the Council but, at the present rate, that hole will soon be filled. We shall have to keep in touch with all these wonderful young men in case we can fit them in somewhere, if not in this, in another diocese. I have hopes in that direction although I dare not mention it until it materializes. Then there are the unreformed Cistercians; they are so unreformed that they are open to anything. The Abbot, a splendid type of real bog Irishman, called on me on Tuesday. He did not have a fit when I suggested his opening a totally unreformed Priory. All he said was: "If we did, to be sure none would be left in the Abbey." He is a tremendous chap but a very slow mover. I shall be dead long before he has sorted that one out. He is doubtless chewing it over as a cow the cud.

That is enough for tonight. Do not forget to say a prayer in propitiation for all the evil I have done. I am haunted by the sallow face of the young man whose vocation I ruined.

◇   ◇   ◇

28.   Second letter to George Weir, Archbishop of Derby.
     (The first is #7.)
Monday, January 31st, 1977.

Dear George,

Last week you wrote to me in confidence. This week I return the compliment.

I have decided to reopen the diocesan seminary. Charles Bouverie has accepted the Rectorship. Yesterday and Saturday he and I interviewed twenty candidates. We rejected nine and accepted eleven, five ex-seminarians and six starters. We shall be interviewing a further fifteen next weekend, February

5/6th, and some more on 12/13th since applications are still coming in. This surprises me since I am supposed to be on the verge of death, but there it is.

Normally Stamford cannot absorb more than an average of four ordinations a year, that is, allowing for wastage, six entrants. It is true that at the moment, owing to the shortage, I could absorb six ordinations and say nine entrants. Obviously, however, I do not want them all starting in the same year so as to leave me no room for the future. It is therefore clear that I shall have to reject the majority of candidates over the next fortnight. Of the remaining twenty or more to be interviewed I shall be unable to take more than three. That with the six entrants I have already accepted would give me nine starters in September plus two certainties and perhaps more from the diocese of Stamford itself. What is to happen to the rest? No matter how authentic their vocation, I simply have no room for them.

Will you take any?

There are, of course, snags:

1. All these vocations are for the Old Religion.

2. The seminary will give the traditional training in philosophy and theology (but the former more intelligently done) plus a serious course on prayer and mystical theology, etc.

3. All students must join the Secular Institute of St John Fisher by which they bind themselves after ordination to celebrate the Immemorial Mass at least once a week privately and once a month on a Sunday. If the bishop prohibits this, they are bound to resign and the Institute is bound to provide for them. They must subscribe to the Institute against such an eventuality.

Of course in practice the difficulty is going to be to get the young men ever to say anything which remotely smells of the New Ordo. But for most of them ordination will still be five years away, by which time much may have changed. Anyway, they will at least be familiar with my hybrid Mass as they will get it twice a week at the seminary.

There is another problem, but I doubt if it is of the sort which would worry you. There is too much deviousness and secrecy in the post-Conciliar church, far more than there used to be of old. I am unwilling to accept students nominally for Stamford but with the proviso that they may be incardinated into another, anonymous diocese. This will not do. If you want any of the students, I must be able to interview openly for the two dioceses of Stamford and Derby. One of the lads whom I have already accepted and one whom I have rejected were born in your diocese. Of the certain applicants still to be seen, one is Derby born and another Derby domiciled; both will be interviewed between 11 a.m. and 1 p.m. on Saturday next. Can you come or will you delegate somebody to inspect them?

I should much like to talk to you about all this. The trouble is that I am not easily movable. But you can ring me up now; I am no longer off the phone.

◇   ◇   ◇

29. Second letter to Monsignor Testastorta at the Apostolic Delegation.
(The first is #2.)
Tuesday, February 1st, 1977.

Dear Monsignor,
You say that you have received a complaint that money subscribed to the diocese of Stamford has been misappropriated to a body called The Tridentine Trust. This body is not yet legally constituted and its name may be changed. Its acting chairman is the Dowager Duchess of Blackwater. I suggest that you direct your complaint direct to Her Grace's solicitors, Messrs Gote, Gote and Kydd, Parade Mansions, Stamford. They will, of course, be interested to know the source of your complaint.

However, my dear Monsignor, I cannot adequately express my delight that you should be turning your attention to the misappropriation of ecclesiastical funds. It is among the most shocking scandals in the post-Conciliar church. It runs through everything, from the sublime to the ridiculous. I shall give you a tiny but typical example.

Last year I was invited to attend the centenary celebrations of the church at Grumby. I had been Parish Priest there from 1947 to 1956. The church itself is among the better examples of Victorian Gothic, spacious, dignified and not over-ornate. It contained, however, a great many very beautiful and valuable objects. Most of these had come from the private chapel of a Recusant family, the Sullyards, who gave them to the parish when they sold Grumby Hall in the late 1920s.

My intention had been to sit in the choirstalls during Mass. Silly of me: the stalls, fine Jacobean ones from the Hall, had gone; so had the altar, the crucifix, the reredos. In fact the whole choir had gone! A partition separated it from the nave and a low ceiling put in: it was a room for "encounter and discussion." In the nave, the solid oak pews had vanished. The Communion Trestle stood in the middle surrounded by chairs with no kneelers. The magnificent Lady Altar and statue of Our Lady had disappeared from the South transept, as had the Sacred Heart Altar from the North. No pulpit, of course, although it was a rare piece of figured walnut dated 1704. No Stations of the Cross, no crucifix, no statues. The only sign of religion was the Sacred Microphone.

Before the ceremony started I hunted round for the Blessed Sacrament. It was no longer kept in the church. A door had been pierced from the South transept into the presbytery and what had been my study had become the "Sacrament Chapel." Thus was removed the Unwanted Presence.

In due course, some twenty co-celebrants, each doubtless with a stipend in his pocket, emerged in the usual sackcloth nightgowns. This surprised me as Grumby must possess one of the finest collections of vestments in the country: some early Renascence with unbelievable orphreys but most 18th century, either Lyons damask or Venetian embroidery. There were twelve solid silver chalices and nine ciboria of varying sizes. All were good: one late medieval English chalice, circa 1470, another Roman Renascence of about 1520, etc.; a vast Spanish ciborium dated 1610. None of these were used but two glazed earthenware goblets with plates to match and a similar large salad bowl by way of ciborium.

I need not describe the ceremony.

When it was over, the clergy forgathered for drinks in the presbytery. Knowing the geography, I went round the back way through the garden. There I discovered what had happened to the statue of Our Lady—a fine piece of Carrara marble in the style of Thorwaldsen. It had become a caryatid supporting a broken end of the chicken-hutch. The path, too, was flagged in white marble which I took to be the remains of the High Altar.

I entered the dining room through the French windows. In front of me was the sideboard, laden with drinks. It was the Lady Altar, a magnificent specimen of Bavarian rococo wood-carving dated 1762; it had come from the Hall. The reredos from the High Altar had been cut up into small pictures and decorated the walls.

My host came forward to greet me. A handsome man and he looked very smart. I could not help but admire the fringe of the handkerchief in his breastpocket. I rapidly put on my spectacles. It was exquisite drawn-thread work. I recognised it. "Congratulations, Father," I said, "I see you have found a use for those old corporals." "Yes," he answered without a qualm, "I thought it a pity to throw them away."

In the course of the jolly celebrations I discovered what had happened to most of the stuff. The cost for "renewing" the church had largely been met by the Sullyard crucifix over the High Altar—English polychrome wood circa 1500 which was bought by the Victoria and Albert Museum for £9,500. The "Sacrament Chapel" and presbytery were paid for out of the chalices and ciboria. "Do you remember the rickety old V shaped chalice, my Lord [doubtless the mediaeval one]? Well, they gave me £2,000 for it. The enormous ciborium was disappointing; I only got £600. But the small one with cherubs round it fetched over £1,000. Extraordinary what ignorant people will pay for rubbish!"

I inquired about the Sacred Heart altar and Stations. "We did not have to pay a penny to get rid of them. A parishioner carted them off free to the municipal dump. I believe in giving the laity something to do." "And the vestments?" I inquired with some trepidation. "I've kept a set of decent new ones for visiting priests. I was extraordinarily lucky with the rest. I swapped them for the two most up-to-date coloured television sets in the country, one for the housekeeper, one for myself. They are years old now but they are still the best. Come and have a look, my Lord."

Enough!

Now, my dear Monsignor, is there no misappropriation in such a case? You know that I was appointed to Stamford because I have a vague idea of the monetary value of things. Very well, apart from misuse (the rococo side-board and Carrara caryatid), I value the objects sold or destroyed at over £70,000. This was a capital investment increasing in value. Perhaps £5,000 was spent on needed repairs to church and presbytery, which should have come out of revenue. Perhaps another £5,000 was spent on semi-durables such as chairs and microphones in the church and carpets and televisions in the presbytery, the eventual value of which is nil. The fact remains that there has been misappropriations of £70,000 in money. One cannot give a figure for misappropriation in spiritualities—the Real Absence, the Sacred Heart, Our Lady, the Stations and the like. Yet, even in terms of money, they are the more important, since the revenue of the church depends on the devotion of the people. I repeat in capitals: THE REVENUE OF THE CHURCH DEPENDS ON THE DEVOTION OF THE PEOPLE. At Grumby the revenue will inevitably dry up and the capital has been squandered.

This is happening all over England. I believe it is even worse in your native Italy. I quote Grumby merely because it is well known to me but there are equally shattering examples in my own diocese of Stamford. I have tried to put a stop to it but with scant success. Why? Because it really depends on the priorities in the mind of the clergy, on the piety of priests in fact. At the moment they are willing to swap vestments for television; what we need is priests who will swap their television for vestments.

I hope I have made myself clear so far because at long last I have come to my main point: the New Religion is living off the capital of the Old. It has not had to provide churches, schools or institutions of any sort—and practically no priests. All was found. Even the cost of destroying the Old has been paid for out of the capital it had accumulated. Once this capital is spent, and it has not far to go, the institutional Church in this country will be bankrupt.

You know that I am not exaggerating. Since 1965 our overall revenue has fallen by about 30% in currency. The currency has devalued by about 50%. In real terms, therefore, the revenue of Roman Catholicism (Great Britain) Ltd is probably about 35% of what it was twelve years ago. This disastrous state of affairs has been partially masked because the overall revenue of R.C. (G.B.) Ltd up to the early 1960s was nearly three times its current expenditure. Hence it could build and maintain churches and schools, monasteries and convents, hospitals and homes, etc. Even in a small parish such as Grumby there was no difficulty in paying off the debt for a 240-place Primary School built in 1939/40 without any government grant whatsoever. The fall in revenue has meant that there is still just about enough to meet current expenditure but none for major maintenance of buildings, new projects or the cost of "renewal." Any deficit is bound to be made good by misappropriation of capital. This does not only occur in small parishes like Grumby. If you really intend, my dear Monsignor, as I sincerely hope you do, to examine misappropriation of ecclesiastical funds, I suggest that you begin with the sale of the Montagnas from the sacristy of Westminster Cathedral.

To be dead serious, Mgr Testastorta, I am absolutely terrified. Here in England we still have two enormously valuable capital assets: our churches and our schools, both paid for by the Old Religion. The churches are falling round our ears for lack of money to maintain them. In the schools we have neither the children nor the staff even if we knew what to teach. Inevitably they will go. Who will buy them? There is only one purchaser: the State. What belongs to God will be sold to Caesar. Then at last Ecumenism will triumph, as the Universal Church becomes a loose federation of National Establishments.

However, let us return to the less serious matter of misappropriation of funds by the Duchess of Blackwater. Her defence is likely to be that the object of the Trust is precisely to avoid misappropriation by the clergy. In my first paragraph I advised you to write to her solicitors. I retract: I strongly disadvise you to do so. Her Grace is a rather formidable woman. Once she gets her teeth into anything she is liable to chew away—as women will—until it is reduced to pulp. I should hate to hear going the rounds the little pleasantry:

> And what's become of Testastorta?
> He acted as he hadn't ought ta
> And like a lamb was led to slaughta
> By the Duchess of Blackwata.

That would not do at all!

◇   ◇   ◇

30. Second letter to the Very Reverend Mother Provincial
Veronican Sisters, London.
(The first letter is #14.)

Thursday, February 3rd, 1977.

Dear Mother Provincial,

First of all may I say how much I admire you for having
stuck to your guns? So often good people are willing to compromise what is right out of humility, obedience, in search
of peace; whereas the wicked hold firm to evil. This latter
point is well illustrated by your Council. What determination
in support of the charismatic nuns! The scandal is not
Sludge's Eucharist but my interference. It is not the white-
slacked nuns who are to blame but you for blaming them. It
is all exactly upside-down.

I knew that convents were in a pretty good mess but it
is difficult from the outside to tell exactly how terrible the
situation is. It is true that nuns' faces have all changed.
Mother Battleaxe and Sister Appleface no longer exist. All
look drawn and strained. At first I put it down to the fact that
we could now see you properly. Of old we could only see a
timeless beak protruding from starch. Now we can see the
whisp of lifeless hair, the ravaged neck, the shrinking calf.
How cruel it all is. That alone made me doubt the intention
of your reformers: no good intention is ever cruel. Do you
remember Abbess Bertha of the Canonesses at Sandborough?
I was terrified of her. How magnificent she looked in her great
black habit and that tower of starch on her head. Like the
rest, she was reformed. She turned out to be a poor old duck
of over 80 with knobby feet, bow legs which could scarcely
support her, and a huge flabby goitre. She did not survive
long.

Incidentally, you confirm a very interesting thing she
told me shortly before her death. "A few years ago only one
nun took sleeping tablets—old Mother Marie, aged about 90.
She slept all day and complained that she could not sleep at
night. All the rest were as healthy and quarrelsome as star-
lings. Now they all have the doctor in at the drop of a rosary.
He prescribes tranquillizers of one sort or another. I am so
ashamed of the quantity consumed that I take the prescrip-
tions round to different chemists in the town so that none
will know that we are a den of addicts." And that, you say,

113

is very much what the Veronican Sisters have become: a set of nervous wrecks.

Yes, alas! it is not merely the habit which has changed; it is the underlying person. Mother Battleaxe has flaked away with rust. Sister Appleface withered when the maggot reached the core. From the serene they have become nervous, from gay sullen, from sweet bitter. And, poor dears, some of them try so desperately to be the same. The mask just covers what is not there.

I realize now, too late, that the revolutionaries started their attack on you nuns. It was away back in the '50s. There were those biblical and theological courses, leading to internal degrees, which were organized in the convents. I noticed that the "professors" were often of questionable orthodoxy but it never crossed my mind that they dished out to the nuns what they might let drop to a fellow priest. And there was no means of controlling what they dished out. Then nuns have lots of days of recollection and retreats—heaven-sent gifts for implanting the maggot into Sister Appleface. After I became bishop I stopped one handsome young Jesuit from giving retreats to nuns in my diocese. Not only was I too late but he became idealized as the victim of a tyrant.

Yes, the revolutionaries had it all planned. The nuns educated the future mothers and "the hand which rocks the cradle rules the world." They were absolutely right. Silly men like me allowed it to go on. The nuns, we thought, are far too sensible to swallow such rubbish; but we never gave them any other food. Swallow it they did, at first like goodies and now like tranquillizers. We are starting to witness the result: it is the women rather than the men who have lost the Faith. But I am wandering, as usual.

So your dear Council has written to Rome to ask for your deposition. You have revealed yourself in your true colours as a traditionalist in opposition to the Holy Father and the Council. I think a man would have resigned on the spot—at least I should. That is where you women have so much more moral courage: you will wait until you are deposed. The mechanism, you tell me, will take about three months, until Easter. I doubt it: Testastorta will hurry that one through in four weeks. Anyway, while you still can you will sell me Horethorpe—the Hall, the Court and the 84 acres. Your surveyor says that it is worth at least £260,000 in four lots—but it might take some time to sell it. The minimum for an immediate sale is £200,000. It seems to me dirt cheap—and you throw in the contents. Dear me, I most certainly accept. It is most generous of you. I shall see that the deposit is paid on Monday and the contract will be finalized as soon as the solicitors have done their job. I am deeply grateful to you. Incidentally, I love your Council's compromise: they will raise no objection to your selling Horethorpe to me provided you raise no objection to being deposed. Charming women! However, it increases my indebtedness to you.

There is only one untidy end which still needs clearing up: you. You can scarcely remain in a Congregation which has in practice expelled you. An ex-Provincial can be placed but a deposed one is more awkward. I suggest that you quit the Veronican Sisters in order to found the Sisters of the Veil. After all, Veronica is only known by her veil, so you would not be renouncing your allegiance. You would have exactly the same constitution as the Veronican Sisters, which has already been approved by Rome, less some of those lamentable *"petites dévotions"* introduced in the last century. You would wear the habit which they have discarded plus an enormous veil—so becoming. Your Mother House, as a diocesan Congregation, would be the Court at Horethorpe.

Obviously you will have to find a few nuns. This should present no problem. I have already heard from the two Sisters who refused to join Sludge's antics as well as the one who jumped over the wall last year. You doubtless know several more Veronican Sisters who would follow you. I have letters from five nuns who are in near-despair in their own convents—but it would probably be a mistake to take them: they would be much better employed in helping eventually to restore order where they are. I also have no fewer than fifteen letters from young women who have written to ask whether I can guide them to a convent where God is still adored. You might get two or three out of them—although I should deprecate your swiping the lot.

I realize that the Veronican Sisters have become in practice a teaching order. At their foundation this was not so. I think that the Veil, too, should widen its activities. You could doubtless train any subjects suitable to be teachers at Stamford University, but that would be a sideline. Your main activity would be connected with the seminary at the Hall. You

115

would look after its physical welfare. In return the seminary would train you to inculcate High Spirituality in the active orders of nuns throughout the diocese. You would undo the harm done by my "handsome Jesuit" and others. I see no reason why nuns should not preach retreats to nuns: they could not do it worse than it has been done by priests. However, Divine Providence will work this all out: there is no use in our making watertight plans which will turn out to be sieves.

What an astonishing affair all this is! On January 13th I decided to permit the Immemorial Mass. By February 3rd I am engaged in founding a seminary and a religious Congregation for women—so central is the Mass to Catholicism. I wonder what I shall be up to next week? You might say a prayer that I don't collapse. I have got to dine out tonight—which is a great trial.

On the human side you have my gratitude and admiration; on the Divine, you have my blessing and my prayers.

◊   ◊   ◊

31.   Second letter to the Reverend William Harris.
(The first letter is #16.)
Thursday, February 3rd, 1977.

Dear Father Harris,
"Consolation" seems to me a frightfully unctuous word. I should not blame you in the least if you again asked to be excardinated upon my assurance that your letter had caused me "much consolation." No, it caused me joy, gratitude, hope—a thousand high sentiments which I can scarcely disentangle, let alone express.

So you will stick it. You will say the Immemorial Mass. Subjectively it doubtless requires much mortification, humility and piety on your part; but that is precisely what makes your action objectively noble. Nothing is sublime without humility, noble without mortification, beautiful without piety—which is doubtless why so little is sublime, noble and beautiful today. I thank you and admire you. No I don't: that is the wrong way round. I thank God for you; I glorify God on your account.

You know, basically there are only two viable religious attitudes:

that of beating one's breast, mortification = asceticism;
that of glorifying God, totally and absolutely =
contemplation.

In this life they cannot be separated. Contemplation without
asceticism is Quietism. Asceticism without contemplation is
Jansenism. That is why in the Mass the *Kyrie* is immediately
followed by the *Gloria*; why in the *Hanc Igitur* the Sacrifice
of our redemption is called the recognition of our slavery—
oblatio servitutis nostrae.

Therein lies the heresy of the modern age. It denies both
the asceticism of the Jansenists and the contemplation of the
Quietists. It takes the worst of both worlds. There is no talk
of beating one's own breast. At best we beat our neighbors,
at worst we accuse God. There is no talk now of the adoration
of God. At best we adore humanity, at worst ourselves.

One sees it in our buildings. There are churches built for
the *Kyrie*, such as the austere Cistercian Abbeys. There are
those built for the *Gloria*, such as the great cathedrals and
High Baroque. Some are built for both, like the late Roman-
esque and early Renascence. Today they are built for neither:
they are transformed into halls for encounter and dialogue
where the Sacred Microphone is the only ornament.

You mention my third *Ad clerum*—all that rubbish about
Constitutions, Institutions, Notifications and the rest. You are
very kind. But, Father, how I hated writing it. It had to be
done or I should not have bothered. Yet, fancy having to defend the Mass by legal quibbles. What nonsense! It stands
mole sua, by its own imponderable weight. It is the Mass. I
might be prepared to look at a new Mass form if it magnified
God still more and exalted Him still higher; if it lowered man
still further in the imagination of his heart; if the mysteries
appeared more wondrous and the doctrines more luminous;
if the language was more noble and the images grander. But
look what we have been given: the exaltation of man and the
humiliation of God; the evacuation of mystery, and ambi-
guity in doctrine; the flattest of images in pidgin vernacular.
I stuck it for seven years but I can no longer. It is terribly
difficult to analyse one's own motives but I suspect it was
Christmas, less than six weeks ago, which was the last straw.
There at the crib was the infant Christ faced by Adult Christians. God forgive us!

Anyway, how wonderful it is that you should have rediscovered the Mass. I am sure that therein lies the explanation as to why Divine Providence allowed it to be hidden. We took for granted of all things conceivable the most stupendous: the Mass, in which Eternity touches time, the Infinite is circumscribed, the Omnipotent is helpless. Yes, we dared to take it for granted. So, by the authority of His Vicar, His Bishops, His priests, He hid it away—so that we could find it. That is what you and I have done. We shall not easily allow it to be hidden again.

Please remember me in the Memento for the living and, in a few months, in the Memento for the dead.

◊   ◊   ◊

32.   To the Reverend Bryan Houghton,
          Avignon, France.
Thursday, February 3rd, 1977.

Dear Bryan,

I have just got back from the inaugural meeting of the Trust and thought I would let you know how it went before I go to bed.

It was at 6 p.m. at the Duchess's. I arrived on the early side in case the Duchess wanted to talk to me before the meeting, but Outman was already there. He immediately grabbed me: "I am so glad to be invited to sit on this Trust because I thought I was in your bad books." "Good heavens! What on earth made you think that?" I asked. "Well, a couple of months ago you refused to reappoint me as Foundation Governor of the schools at Sandborough." "It was you who resigned because of overwork as Chairman of the County Council." "Rot!" It transpired that he had not resigned at all but that, when his quinquennial appointment came to an end, the secretary of the Schools' Commission, one Father Terence Daly, simply appointed someone else and had the impertinence to write to Outman on my behalf thanking him for his past services. I have just rung up Daly to come and see me tomorrow afternoon. There is some ridiculous mistake but it needs sorting out.

Bouverie had driven me over. Cutting and Solly Glauben arrived practically together. They were a comic pair: Sir John is a lanky, blond Anglo-Saxon; Glauben a diminutive, dark Oriental, but very daintily built and with finely chiselled fea-

118

tures. Luckily the Duchess fell for him immediately. I had feared that she might give her well-known imitation of an iceberg.

The Duchess's solicitors emerged from somewhere and we got down to business. I need not bother you about that as Gote & Co. will send you a copy of the Trust Deed along with other papers for your signature. As you see, they insisted on calling it the "Edmund Forester Trust". The Duchess said: "Tridentine sounds as though we only had three teeth—insufficient to chew up a score of bishops." Thanks to Sir John it did not take long. It is astonishing how amenable solicitors become in the presence of a judge. Instead of the usual hollow laugh and "You can't do that, you know," there was nothing but "Yes, Sir; of course, Sir." The Trust's legal address will be % Gote & Co., who will also act as Secretary and Treasurer so as to avoid accusations that the Trust is embezzling diocesan money. I had a letter from Testa on Tuesday accusing me precisely of that. He seems frightfully well informed as to what goes on at Stamford. He might almost have a spy on the spot!

We then fell to discussing the objects of the Trust. I told them of my intention to re-open the diocesan seminary and to this end had agreed to the purchase of Horethorpe for £200,000 of which we already had half in cash. I gave details of the students I had interviewed and mentioned, perhaps unwisely, that I had hopes that Archbishop Weir and the Cistercians might use it. I also referred to the possibility that some ex-Veronican Sisters might take over the Court. Bouverie gave details concerning the curriculum, staffing and costs. All this was fairly plain sailing and everybody was duly impressed by Bouverie. It was Cutting who asked the awkward question: "And who is to ordain these young men when you die?" I said that I had a promise that it would be done but that I was under an obligation not to reveal who it was. "Is it in writing?" "Well, it was but I was asked to destroy the paper." "Most unsatisfactory!" I had to agree that it was and began to feel very silly. In fact my heart sank into my boots. It was the Duchess who saved the situation. She said it was a risk well worth taking and added: "Besides, the Pope himself would ordain the lads in order to prevent Archbishop Lefebvre from doing so." Cutting thought this frightfully funny "and probably true. If you have got the young men, you will doubtless be able to find an old boy to ordain them." So the seminary was agreed to as our first priority. The Duchess and Glauben would guarantee the overdraft since a mortgage was unnecessary as money was still coming in.

Outman then embarked on his hobby-horse, the schools. His theme song was: "What is the use of Bouverie's priests teaching one thing if the teachers teach the opposite?" He pointed out perfectly correctly that: 1. The bishops have not a clue what is taught in their schools; 2. these are entirely in the hands of an anonymous Schools' Commission and its Inspectors; 3. the bishop does not even know the Governors whom he appoints; 4. the said Governors have not a clue what to do about religious instruction; 5. a heavy percentage of the teachers are non-Catholics; 6. to keep the numbers up, an increasing percentage of the pupils are non-Catholic as well. "To talk of Catholic Schools is a bad joke. Cannot the Trust take them over?"

I said that he was absolutely right but that the Trust could not interfere with Voluntary Aided Schools, i.e. schools within the Government system. They depended entirely on the diocese and the Ministry. I should, however, look seriously into the set-up of the Schools' Commission and the appointment of Governors, etc. "As for the question of staff," I said, "the reason is fairly simple. Teachers like to know what to teach. This, at the moment, is something which Catholic teachers do not know. They therefore prefer to teach in State schools where they will not be required to teach religion. This applies in particular to orthodox Catholics. Hence it is that the teachers we do get tend to be modernist: they know only too well what they want to teach. For the same reason non-Catholics apply to our schools: they will not be required to teach religion. Hence we get the extraordinary paradox that a Confessional School is non-Confessional."

Cutting broke in: "If, my Lord, you saw the situation so clearly, how is it that you did nothing about it? We all know that our schools are in a frightful mess." "For two reasons— offhand—Sir John," I replied. "Firstly, we bishops did not want to see. Imagine yourself a bishop. Everything around you is crumbling fast. Each day brings a new ruin. Each night you lie awake listening to the storm. Are you going to go out of your way to find more trouble? The bricks and mortar of the schools are still there, thank God! But one must not look

120

inside. I do not ask for your pity but I do ask for your comprehension. We have pulled the pack of cards around our heads and our five senses are choked with the wreckage. No longer can we even console ourselves in Holy Mass. It is our fault—but that makes it worse. Secondly, to stop the rot in the schools, one would have to draw the line. But you cannot draw a zig-zag line; it must be straight. We could not now be talking about schools had I not drawn the line about Mass on January 13th. You yourselves take it for granted that the line is straight. I could not have cried halt! on the schools without doing the same for the Mass. I have done so for the Mass, so you take it for granted that I must do so for the schools."

Outman brought us back to schools: "I accept, my Lord, that you will deal with the Commission and the Governors, but what about the teachers? I suggest, as a start, that it be made obligatory for all teachers of catechetics to attend a refresher course each year at Horethorpe." I was rather against the compulsion: it might be anti-productive since it could not be enforced. An annual refresher course in catechetics and a retreat for teachers could certainly be arranged. Bouverie agreed. "But where I think the Trust could be immensely useful," I added, "would be in providing a Catholic Student-Teacher Centre attached to Stamford University Training College. There could be proper courses in catechetics, church history, Scholastic philosophy—the lot. Moreover, I feel sure that Mr Outman will agree (he, like myself, is on the University Board) that the University would recognize it and partly maintain it—so long as it does not have to provide it. But Horethorpe is too remote. What is it, forty miles or more from Stamford? One needs a building on the spot. There is likely to be one. I understand that the Reparationist Fathers intend to leave the diocese and sell their house. It is a hideous Victorian affair in the once residential suburb of Offleigh. Its large garden abuts upon the boundary of the University campus." This, of course, more than fulfilled Outman's wildest dreams. He thought that the Centre was already in existence. The Duchess had to remind him that it was a matter proposed for our consideration and not for immediate execution.

The chairman of the Latin Mass Society, a Mr Villiers who had arrived a bit late, chipped in: "It does seem extraordinary that in the whole of England and Wales there is not a single school in which parents can transmit their religion to their children. The situation is often worse in the private sector than in the public, with which Mr Outman has been dealing." He then gave some frightful examples, some of which I know to be true. "The majority of 'resisters' are not old fogies at all but youngish married couples with children to educate. They want to give to the children they love the religion in which they adore. The bishops—excuse me, my Lord—simper and whimper about 'parental rights' but trample on them with utter heartlessness. It is a heavy price we have to pay for the celibacy of the clergy: the clergy, from Pope to curate, have no conception how we suffer from the cleavage of religion in our own flesh and blood. My last born, a girl, is still at school. I send her to a 'resistance' school in France. I prefer the physical cleavage of a thousand miles to the slightest cleavage in our religion. Can this Trust do nothing in the private sector of education?"

Luckily I did not have to answer straight away. Cutting did it for me. "The trouble is that Catholic private education in this country is almost exclusively in the hands of the clergy—Benedictines, Jesuits, Rosminians, Seculars, Brothers, Nuns; and the few non-clerical preparatory schools are obliged to prepare as is required by the clerical Public Schools and Colleges. There is much talk today about lay participation but here is a field in which the laity are primarily concerned, since they produce the children, but from which they are totally excluded. No matter what the financial backing of the Trust, it would be well nigh impossible to break through the clerical monopoly in private education so long as there are any clergy left."

"Besides," Glauben added, "the Trust draws its funds from public sources and it would not improve our image if the headlines appeared: 'Duchess appeals for education of Solly Glauben's children.' I am more involved than you, Mr Villiers, as I have two little boys to educate and my wife is pregnant. I do intend to do something about it, but I fear it will mean private tuition until such time as the Church comes to her senses—unless Bishop Forester has some bright idea."

I was not really taken by surprise; the problem—and the injustice of it—had often occupied my mind. "I agree entirely with what all three of you have said. But Mr Glauben is right: the Trust itself cannot deal with the private sector in education. A separate committee should be formed, perhaps under the aegis of Mr Villiers and the Latin Mass Society. It would maintain close links with the Trust. Apart from money, I doubt if there would be any difficulty in establishing a 'resistance' school for girls from 9 to 18. Convents are closing down all over the country and it would be easy to find suitable premises. Indeed, some ex-Veronican Sisters might run it but with the ownership firmly in lay hands. It is boys who present the problem and it is here that Sir John's analysis is absolutely correct. There would be no difficulty in finding 'resistance' prep schools if they could feed a 'resistance' Public School; but these are all in clerical hands. Now, the thought has occurred to me that we might be able to come to terms with the old-established but not very successful school at Sockham. It is officially Anglican but, to keep the numbers up, it admits a substantial number of non-Conformists. Its problem, in fact, is numbers rather than money, since it is fairly heavily endowed. It would be likely to jump at the prospect of having a Catholic house provided the intake were over twenty a year. Games and classes would be in common, as is work and leisure in adult life; the environment of the house, religious instruction and worship, would be entirely separate, as again in adult life. It would be mixed-Confessional and in no way ecumenical. This, to my mind, is precisely what is wanted. I may add that the Chairman of Governors is our hostess's son, the Duke of Blackwater—please don't interrupt. As I have said, there would be no difficulty in finding 'resistance' prep schools if there were a Public School which they could feed. Indeed, I am quite certain that the only lay owned Catholic prep school in the diocese would welcome the suggestion. I repeat: this is not a matter in which the Trust can be directly involved but it may give food for thought to Mr Villiers and Mr Glauben."

"Indeed it will," said the Duchess, "and if you want anybody to put out feelers at Sockham and lay prep schools, I have your man, although he is not a Catholic. It is not my son but my brother-in-law. He will probably drop in for a drink after dinner. He would do anything to save Sockham. It's his old school."

At this point the butler rolled in the drinks and the Duchess said the meeting was closed; dinner would be served in exactly thirty minutes. "But I want to mention fund-raising,"

Glauben expostulated. "We can talk about that at dinner," replied the Duchess. "I shall let Forester know what transpires over the phone. He prefers to absorb his beastly diet at home. I shall see you all in half an hour," and she disappeared.

I chatted a bit to Glauben and Villiers, neither of whom I had met before. Glauben is even more impressive in his person than in his letters. We made a date to meet privately, on Sunday week, along with Mrs Glauben. Old Gote stayed for dinner, so the Duchess's chauffeur drove me home.

Incidentally, she rang me up an hour ago to say that Glauben is launching a national appeal. He is sending his publicity photographer down on Monday. The Duchess has got to be dressed as though she were old Queen Mary "and dripping with pearls: no diamonds—they're vulgar and will do for my wife but not for a duchess." I must have mitre, cope "and those ridiculous gloves, so as to look like a bejewelled beetle." He says he will eat his hat if he does not get over a quarter of a million. I hope it is edible.

So that, my dear Bryan, is that. The seminary at Horethorpe is safe. Outman will see to it that the Teachers' Centre becomes a reality. When I left he was talking with Bouverie about staffing and the curriculum. He is a bit of a bulldozer— but that is what is wanted. Anyway, they all seem absolutely determined to make a go of the Trust, and none of them are people who can be easily brushed aside. I go to bed with far more confidence than I did last night.

A thousand thanks for your letter of the 26th. . . .

◊　◊　◊

33.　To Dean Nial McCarthy, Parish Priest of Horebury.
(Author of the report on Father Roderic Sludge.)
Friday, February 4th, 1977.

My dear Dean,
A clear case of telepathy: I was on the point of writing to you when your letter arrived. First allow me to deal with my own business, then I shall answer you.

I confirm the postscript to my *Ad clerum* No. 3: Mgr Bouverie will re-open the diocesan seminary, probably after Easter. What is news is that a Trust under the chairmanship of the Dowager Duchess of Blackwater is in the process of buying the Horethorpe estate off the Veronican Sisters for that purpose. The seminary will therefore be in your deanery, so you are the first person who should be told. There is nothing secret about this. On the contrary, I should be grateful if you would inform the other Deans of the diocese as well as your own priests. It will save me another *Ad clerum*.

The two nuns who would have nothing to do with Sludge have written to me to say that they refuse to move out of the Hall. Please tell them that I shall be writing to them in due course but, in the meantime, I should be most grateful if they vacated the Hall and moved into the Court. They can keep one set of keys for the Hall and give you the rest plus one set of keys for the Court. They may already have heard from their splendid Mother Provincial.

Bouverie and I invite ourselves to lunch on Tuesday, unless you phone to the contrary. Don't prepare anything for me as I bring my diet in a thermos. Bouverie is a great trencher man but is more interested in quantity than quality: lots of potatoes and bananas. I have noticed before that intellectuals are voracious but undiscriminating, whereas gourmets, although highly sensitive, are often pretty dim: they keep their brain in their stomach. Having said that, I cannot remember if you are a gourmet; I have certainly had some delicious meals at Horebury when I could eat them. Anyway, after lunch we can all three wander round Horebury. It will be a wonderful change for me who have been chained to my desk for three weeks.

Incidentally, I enclose the keys to the chapel. Would you be so very kind as to break the seals, unlock it and exorcize it in the simple form? If you have not time between now and Tuesday, we can do it then. I doubt if it will ever be used as a chapel again. It is for Bouverie to decide, but I suspect that the gym would make a far finer chapel—especially if the Duchess (as I rather hope) induces her son to furnish it with some of the magnificent junk from Blackwater Place.

That, I think, is all I wanted to say. I can now answer your letter.

I am delighted to learn that everything is working so well. Mind you, you are lucky in that both your curates are co-operative. It is very awkward when, as at . . ., one of them is leader of the opposition. It is early to say whether the rise in Mass attendance is going to be permanent or whether it is due to the enormous amount of publicity we have received. It is kind of you to say that I came over all right on television. I do not possess that instrument so I have not seen myself. Your rise in the collections seems to be abnormal; some of it must be "thanksgiving" money which will not be repeated. I am most interested to learn that your people should appear to want either the Old Mass or my hybrid, but nobody wants the New Ordo. However, in answer to your direct question, I should advise you to keep one New Ordo celebration on a Sunday until you are quite certain that it is not wanted. As I said in my *Ad clerum*, I should hate to treat the New Massers as they treated the Old.

You raise the problem of house Masses and little groups. You are not the only one and I may have to issue a circular about it. No, a far better idea: you can write a paper on the subject which will be the "case for discussion" at the next Deanery Meetings. Let me have it within the fortnight so that I have time to circulate it. I should just like to bring the following points to your attention:

1. The natural group is precisely the parish, which gathers ideally at the Parish Church around the Real Presence of the Redeemer.

2. Chapels of Ease, of which you have three including the Convent, do not break the unity of the group since it is clear to all that they exist out of geographical necessity, not because of human divergence.

3. The New Ordo, on the other hand, depends for its effectiveness on human participation which differs widely according to natural aptitudes and educational background.

4. It is therefore natural that the New Ordo should splinter the parish into its constituent human groups, which the parish had unified.

5. This splintering process inevitably leads to the "elitism" of little groups and house Masses, of which you had such a striking example in the Sludge case.

All this seems to me straightforward and common sense. It therefore follows that so long as you used the New Ordo you could only make it vital through house Masses, with the consequent disintegration of the parish. Since the Immemorial Mass has been reintroduced, which requires no more than the confrontation of the two presences, human and Divine, the parish regains its unity, with the consequent collapse of the house Mass and the elitist groups. I see this as inevitable. You will not have to suppress the house Masses; they will disappear of their own accord. In another month or so the faithful will not want them and the priests won't say them. However, objectively their disappearance is to be encouraged since sanctity, not participational aptitude, is the only elitism known to Christianity.

You also ask me about "caring communities." I must frankly admit that I know nothing about them. I took it for granted that they were the folk who insisted on house Masses. Are they a separate entity? How little a bishop knows of what goes on in his diocese! Last November I was invited to attend a jamboree of "caring communities" in London. It was all about South Africa and apartheid. I presumed that was because the Soweto riots were still news. At the end I was asked to say a few words. I said that I had expected to attend a conference of Religious Communities caring for the aged and handicapped, not a conference of experts on South Africa. I wondered if there was a "caring community" in Soweto discussing the mugging, thugging and drugging in London. I also suggested that they might care for the souls of the couple of million non-Christian coloured immigrants in our midst, etc. This was apparently quite the wrong thing to say and the situation was only saved by the chairman assuring the carers that I had an inverted sense of humour.

Anyway, from that one experience I gained the impression that they were not caring *for* anybody but *about* something, which is a very different proposition, no matter how laudable. To "care for" means to do something or to love somebody; to "care about" implies no more than talk seasoned with moral indignation. The former always has as its object a reality, the latter always an abstract idea—usually Justice and Peace.

Curiously enough, I think that we are here in the presence of the fundamental difference of attitude, in the moral field, between the Old and the New religion. By replacing "caring for" with "caring about," one has substituted moral indignation for charity. This in turn implies the substitution of politics for morality. Penal or political law takes the place of moral law. Crime against the community replaces sin against God. I have no intention of lecturing you on so vast a subject. I merely want to point out the difference in the personal attitude which the change implies.

In the Old religion, we spent out time beating our own breasts, *mea maxima culpa*. We were terribly conscious of our own basic imperfection, of Original Sin in fact. And how deeply felt was our need for a Redeemer! It was neither God's creation nor His Church which needed reforming, it was I. I had no pretension to "do good" because to do good is a prerogative of God. Sufficient for me to avoid evil, of which I am perfectly capable but, by His grace, can overcome. I even lacked the ambition to convert the world: God would see to that, although I could help in some mysterious way by first converting myself. Etc. . . . Such was my attitude on the day of my ordination. Was yours, Nial McCarthy, much different?

What is the attitude now? The first requisite of moral indignation is to accuse your neighbour: *tua culpa*—it is all your fault, your most grievous fault. Original Sin has vanished: it is I who am the Immaculate Conception and Jesus is not my Redeemer but my friend. Everything needs reforming because there is no natural Law in nature; I introduce the Law by the way I use it. My conscience makes the Law, which is as constantly evolving as is nature itself. In the same way, everything in the Church needs reforming, sacraments, structures, the lot, because inevitably in my experience the only constant factor is I. It is even I who am the Real Presence since it is I who invoke His name. To avoid evil is nonsense; on the contrary, I "do good" by the mere process of fulfilling my personality. The conversion of the world is a simple, technical process: the reign of Justice and Peace. Etc. . . .

Have I overdrawn the attitude? Look carefully. I think not. All I have done is to give it precision.

To return to your "caring communities," you know more about them than I. If they are what I fear they are then just like the house Masses they will die out of their own accord. They are a product of the New religion. As the tide of the Old sweeps back, they will be washed away into the abyss of the ocean.

I much look forward to seeing you on Tuesday.

CHAPTER V

TREASON AND TRUST

34.   To the Reverend Bryan Houghton,
            Avignon, France.
Sunday, February 6th, 1977.

Dear Bryan,

I have been hurt where it hurts most, in my friendship. I must tell you the whole story.

I wrote to you on Thursday evening and told you how, at the foundation meeting of the Trust, I learned that a trustee called Outman had been removed from the Governorship of the Catholic schools in the Sandborough area. I presumed there was some misunderstanding. I asked the secretary of the Diocesan Schools' Commission, a Father Terence Daly, to come and see me, without telling him what it was about. He came early on Friday afternoon.

I told him that I had recently seen Mr Outman who had shown me a letter signed by him, Daly, in which I thanked Outman for his past services but was not renewing his appointment as Governor. Daly was obviously taken completely by surprise. He went as white as a sheet and mumbled something about the incompatibility of being chairman of the County Council and Governor of denominational schools. "Nonsense," I said, "and you know it." I waited for some

129

other explanation. It did not come. He just sat there mute. "You have no explanation?" Still no answer. "Very well, Fr Daly, you know that this sort of thing cannot be done. I dismiss you from the Schools' Commission as from this moment. I shall find a suitable post for you in due course," and I rang the bell for FitzHenry so that he would put the dismissal in writing on the spot.

As Fitz entered the room the wretched Daly went completely hysterical, shivering, sobbing, choking, muttering something about "only myself to blame," until he collapsed in a faint on the floor. Fitz and I had not a clue what to do. We dragged him to the sofa and put a rug over him. As soon as he showed signs of life, Fitz administered the universal English medicine, a stiff one. When he could move, we got him to go and lie down on a bed upstairs. He reappeared at about 5 p.m. and said he had something important to tell me. I said I was prepared to listen but should like Fitz to be present to take notes. He raised no objection. This is his story. I edit it a bit because it came out in jerks without following any logical sequence.

There was a small group of like-minded, forward-looking priests who met for lunch at the Stag, Wooton-Bassett, on the third Tuesday of each month. The leader was Canon Cocksedge and the initiates were Daly, Sludge, Harris, N . . ., X . . . and Y . . . This, as a matter of fact, I knew and was grateful to Socks for keeping an eye on the advance guard; what I did not know was that Daly was a member. The object of the group was to bring the diocese up to date in spite of the Bishop by direct influence on the clergy and by getting progressive priests into executive positions. "If you examine the people who surround you, my Lord, you will find that you have only appointed two, Mgr Defew and Fr FitzHenry, against the advice of Canon Cocksedge." This is true. "That does not mean that the V.G., the Chancellor and the rest are members of our group, but they know to whom their appointment is due and will do as they are told. You may remember how upset the Canon was that Fr FitzHenry should be appointed secretary instead of myself, with Sludge at the Schools' Commission?" I did, and could not understand why. Ecclesiastical politics never crossed my mind; I had just thought Sludge unsuitable for the schools and Fitz too young.

It was, apparently, on the third Tuesday of November,

the 17th, that this little gang decided to clean up the schools in the Sandborough area. These schools, four Lower, two Middle and one Upper, had all been reorganised in 1967 and the Governors and Managers came up for re-appointment in block on January 1st, 1977. Cocksedge said it was impossible to get the renewal going in the schools largely because of Mr Outman. He swayed all his colleagues to appoint only the most dismal traditionalists to all specialist posts for cate-chetics. Thus, at the Sacred Heart Upper School there was Exposition once a week; the Rosary was recited; the only hymns taught were the *Salve Regina, Tantum Ergo, Ave Verum* and such like. If he were re-appointed this would go on for another five years since, being chairman of the County Coun-cil, he was far too public a personage for any bishop to dis-miss without scandal. So it was simply decided not to re-appoint him—along with four other Governors if you please! Daly objected that he was running a great risk as any of the rejected Governors might write to the Bishop or he might meet one of them. Socks reassured him by saying: "They will be far too offended to write to him and Forester will not be meeting people much longer as he is dying of cancer. Even if he does find out, you won't be in the dog-house for long before he's dead." Thus was the Outman affair explained.

You may remember that Socks came to stay at Bishop's House to help me out from January 14th onwards. He was in charge of the phone. The third Tuesday was the 18th and indeed he lunched out. I remember it because he was absent for a good long time and I thought it unfair on Fitz. The meeting at the Stag was enlivened by the presence, believe it or not, of Testastorta. All the group were present except Harris whom Socks had put off: "I don't trust that man; he's not ambitious enough." Socks was very despondent. He said the reaction to my *Ad clerum* from laity and clergy had been what one might expect from fools. Worse still, Blythe of Bir-kenhead intended to follow my example and a couple more were shaky. In fact, among the bishops, only Weir seemed solid. He warned Sludge that he was going to be raided on Thursday and had better remove the group's archives to safety. Sludge was the secretary. There seemed to be nothing one could do except to divulge that Forester was a dying man to whom nobody need pay the slightest attention. Sludge un-dertook to write a circular to prove that a bishop had no right to permit the Old Mass. The group was told to lie low and obey the *Ad clerum* until things straightened out with the bishop's death. Testa never opened his mouth during the meeting but took copious notes. He stayed for lunch and entertained everybody with backstairs stories from Rome. After lunch he and Socks disappeared together, leaving the rest to disperse.

During all this—and it lasted an hour and a half—I scarcely interrupted Daly at all. However, when he said that Sludge was the anonymous Canon Lawyer responsible for the circular on the Mass, I pointed out that Cocksedge had practically written the answer for me. This seemed to me to contradict his story. "No it doesn't," Daly answered. "The Canon dislikes and perhaps fears Sludge. He feels himself to be a figurehead whereas Sludge is in contact with really important people. The Canon would enjoy showing him up."

When Daly had finished I said to him: "Father, you have made very serious accusations against a respected priest of this diocese. You can scarcely expect me to take your word for it, especially as you have an interest to shift the blame in the Outman affair. Do you think that any of the priests you have mentioned would corroborate what you have said?"

He was silent for several minutes. I feared that he would have another attack of hysteria. Finally he said: "Harris would corroborate for November but he was not present in January. To ask N . . ., X . . . or Y . . . would probably lead to trouble and scandal. Just ring up the Canon. You know him better than I. He is not the sort of man to deny things. If he does, I am content to be a liar."

I looked at Fitz. "I think we owe it to Father Daly to do as he wishes," he said. I wrote out the text of what I wanted to say: "Fr Daly tells me that it is you who informed the press that I am dying of cancer. You have also revealed the contents of my private correspondence to Mgr Testastorta. It was with your approval that Fr Sludge wrote the circular from the anonymous Canon Lawyer. I am unwilling to believe these wild accusations without corroboration. Have they any basis in fact?" I rang up from my study, Fitz had the receiver off in his office and took down the answer in shorthand: "Of course, Edmund, they are true. Daly has his faults but is not a liar. If you act without consulting your friends, you must expect them to react without consulting you. I hope the old health is all right. It has been a lovely day at Sandborough.

Good night! God bless you," and he put the receiver down. Never a flap, never a shake in his voice. The end of twelve years' intimate friendship meant nothing to him. To me Socks's answer was more terrible than Daly's revelation. So that is that. How well Psalm LIV puts it:

> Had some enemy decried me, I could have borne it patiently;
> Some open ill-wisher, I could have sheltered myself from his attack.
> But thou, my second self, my familiar friend!
> How pleasant was the companionship we shared, thou and I;
> How lovingly we walked as fellow pilgrims in the house of God!

Only last week I hoped that he might be my successor. But now?

I thanked Fr Daly for his honesty and courage. I maintained, however, my decision to reorganise the Schools' Commission and revoke his appointment as secretary. I should like to see him again, now that the Canon has corroborated his statement. He could spend the night at Bishop's House and dine with Fitz. He would have to excuse me as I was on a diet and would go to bed.

That was on Friday. Daly spent the night here and I saw him again next morning before interviewing prospective seminarians.

I shall finish this letter tomorrow.

Monday, February 7th.

You know, my dear Bryan, Daly's story does raise a problem. How far is the revolution in the Church an organized plot? I discussed this with Daly on Saturday morning. It was clear that the Stag group, through its secretary, Sludge, was in correspondence with similar groups in other dioceses. Not only did it subscribe to the reviews one would expect but it also received other matter from diverse sources, principally from Paris. All this was passed round, discussed and eventually filed by Sludge in the group's archives. On the face of it, it looks like an organized plot with its centre in Paris. Cocksedge would be the local executive and Sludge the delegate from the central office. But Daly made a very sensible remark: "Let us suppose that there are plotters in Paris—and there certainly are in the sense that people plot or plan as to how to get their own way—it does not explain how the Stag group got together in Stamford. To my mind the plot theory explains nothing because the plot itself needs explaining. No, it is far simpler than that. Birds of a feather flock together. One merely has to identify the common feather to know which birds will flock. And in the present case the common feather has nothing to do with ideas and ideals. That is the great mistake people make; that is why they cannot understand what is going on. No, it is quite easy to distinguish the common feather from what the birds attack with greatest fury. What has been and continues to be their primary target? It is the structures of the Church, that is to say the normal ladders to promotion and power. What, then, is their primary motive, the common feather? It is self-evident: ambition. I think I told you yesterday the Canon's remark about Fr Harris: 'I don't trust that man: he's not ambitious enough.' That is why I admire the Canon: he is single-mindedly ambitious. He intends to be a bishop. The moment he knew that Stamford would become vacant in the near future, he has done what is necessary to be your successor." "You do not make him out to be a very sincere man," I interrupted. "Sincerity, what's that? He is so sincerely, so conscientiously ambitious that he will sacrifice his religion and his friend to his ambition. Religiously he is far less liberal than you, and you are perhaps the only person in the wide world for whom he feels something akin to affection. Let's leave the Canon. Take me. Why did I join the Stag group? Because I believe in all this progressive rot? Nonsense! No, I joined because it guaranteed promotion and power. I preferred to be secretary to the Schools' Commission to curate at Fenton."

"But Sludge did not get much out of it."

"Oh yes he did! He got the illusion of power, and men are governed far more by their illusions than by reality. And how he must be jeering at you from the safety of Taunton!"

"So you think patronage is the root of the trouble?"

"Not exactly the root but the means of sowing the cockle to smother the wheat. The root trouble in any revolution is precisely that it is rootless. Before the revolution the bishop was obeyed because the structures were intact. All patronage was in his hands and was exercised publicly. The revolution has undermined the structures so that patronage is exercised secretly by pressure groups. There are now two hierarchies, the official and the unofficial. Obviously, only the official is open to attack but unless it exerts itself promptly and firmly—as you, my Lord, are doing—it will simply collapse."

"If your 'Drama of Ambition' can be enacted on the village green of Stamford, one wonders what it must be like in the opera house of Rome! But, although it may explain the Stag pressure group, your theory has nothing to say about the general attitude of the clergy. Why have perfectly decent priests allowed themselves to become the pawns of little men with large ambitions?"

"It is the reverse of the same medal. The structures are collapsing so they have nothing to cling to. Their morale has been undermined and I am pretty certain that ecumenism is the brand of cookie which has choked it. Of old, whatever our faults, we were sincerely jealous and ambitious for our Spouse the Church, just as any married man is for his wife and family. In our attitude to non-Catholics, in *communicatio in sacris*, our jealousy sometimes reached ridiculous proportions, as it will between man and wife. But it was genuinely felt; we were protecting our Immaculate Spouse, the Church in all its beauty, no stain, no wrinkle, no such disfigurement; it was to be holy, it was to be spotless. Ecumenism changed all that. On the authority of the Church herself we were told to share our Hope and our Joy, our true *Gaudium et Spes*, our Spouse, with Tom, Dick and Harry. No longer was She exclusive to me and I to Her. No longer could She be the object of my just jealousy and vaulting ambition. Very well, I had better be jealous and ambitious for my own comfort. It is not an exalted ambition, my Lord, but it is almost the only one the clergy has left—apart, of course, from politics."

"I think, my dear Father," I said, "that some of the Canon's cynicism has brushed off on you. Tell me: in a few months' time he will be your bishop; you have certainly burnt the boat of your ambition with him. What do you intend to do?"

"For some weeks now, I have been thinking of joining the Cistercians at Deepdale. I suppost it is the least contaminated abbey in the country."

"So you are not as cynical as you make out. Father Abbot will be here in half an hour. If you want to meet him, you can stay for lunch."

So much for Daly. There is a great deal in what he says although it may need putting into context and perspective.

I certainly agree that patronage is one of the great dangers in modern society, both civil and ecclesiastic. The Prime Minister of England or President of France are monarchs far more absolute than was ever Louis XIV because they exercise more patronage. Somehow patronage should be separated from government as the legislature is from the judicature. That was the justification for hereditary offices and peerages: they limited patronage. The problem is even more complex in the Church. The Apostles clearly hit on the right idea at the very start when they chose Matthias by lot. Put a score of reasonable names in mitre, draw one out and put the mitre on his head. In one fell swoop patronage would disappear as would ecclesiastical ambition; moreover, no bishop could imagine that he had acquired his mitre on merit. As it is, Socks will succeed me thanks to the patronage of Testastorta and because he is ambitious. He may even feel that he deserves his mitre in compensation for his subservience to authority and treason to his friend.

One little point arises out of all this. When he becomes bishop, Socks will be in a position to destroy all my correspondence. I do not think he should be allowed to. One day it may be important to keep the record straight. I am consequently sending you a parcel containing copies of all my letters since January 16th. I shall keep the file up to date each week. I know they will not be in your way. You can publish them after my death if you think it expedient but please do not destroy them until peace is restored to Holy Church.

The betrayal of Socks was a terrible blow to me but, as is His wont, God gave me compensation. Both Weir and the Abbot rang up to say that they would at least have a look at the sort of men I was interviewing. They arrived before 11 a.m. on Saturday to determine the mechanism by which we could give choice of diocese or of the Cistercians to any suitable candidate. The Abbot then tackled Weir over ordinations: "Dr Forester will soon be among the angels. What is the use of my accepting a novice if I cannot guarantee his ordination? No, Your Grace, your word is not enough. No, no! Here is the form which my chapter requires you to sign before it allows me to take on a lad." It was a promise that Weir would ordain upon presentation by the Abbot. Weir was furious but finally gave in "provided you promise not to reveal it until you have to use it." He then turned to Defew: "I suppose if I make such a promise to this bog Abbot I ought to do the same for your bogus Institute." He wrote it out then and there and handed it to Defew. In return for this noble gesture I promised to surrender the Derby seminarian I had accepted the previous week, provided he was willing. Of the men we then interviewed, Weir took on both the ones from Derby and another. I accepted a charming youth of 18 and a convert parson. The Abbot invited four to see what went on in a Cistercian Abbey.

I notice that in this morning's post there is at last a letter from the Apostolic Delegate in Rome. I shall not bother to read it until after Glauben's photographer has taken me as a bejewelled beetle.

Ah! my dear Bryan, I am so sad about Socks. What a terrible thing ambition is. We must go down on our knees and thank God that neither of us has it.

◊　◊　◊

35.　To Archbishop Josef Klushko
　　　Apostolic Delegate to Great Britain
　　　% Palazzo delle Congregazioni, Rome.
Monday, February 7th, 1977.

Dear Archbishop Klushko,

I am deeply moved to learn that His Holiness should take a personal interest in the state of my health. It is true that I am not expected to live very long but my condition is more inconvenient than painful and my mind is in no way affected.

It is very kind of His Holiness to suggest that I should unburden myself of the care of my diocese. Please assure His Holiness that it is the inspiration of his example which gives me the courage to labour in the Lord's vineyard to the bitter end.

Believe me, my dear Archbishop,
Your Grace's obedient servant in Dmno,

✴Edmund.

P.S. To your official letter you were kind enough to add a personal postscript. I follow your example.

You write: "I am sorry to learn that your distinguished and fruitful career as bishop should end on a tragic note of defiance and rebellion."

"Defiance and rebellion" are not the right words.

137

"Indignant opposition" would be nearer the mark. My attitude is summed up in Psalm XXXVIII:

> It was my resolve to live watchfully, and never use my
> tongue amiss;
> Still, while I was in the presence of sinners,
> I kept my mouth gagged, dumb and patient, impotent
> for good.
> But indignation came back
> And my heart burned within me, the fire kindled by my
> thoughts,
> So that at last I kept silence no longer.

Yes, indignant I am at the ruin of the Church around me. The Immaculate Spouse has been deserted while her votaries fondle the Harlot of the World. Our altars are gone and sacrifice is banished. No longer do the priests cry "Spare, O Lord, spare thy people." The child knows no prayers and the youth no doctrine. Young men and virgins are deaf to God's calling. Old men and widows are bereft of consolation. Who would not be indignant at such desolation?

And all this in little more than a decade. And what does the Administration do about it? With what little authority it has left it hastens the decomposition. It is wreathed in smiles to those who destroy. It accuses of rebellion those who try to preserve. It beats every breast but its own when faced with calamity. Of course I am in opposition.

You know, my dear Archbishop, I fully accept that Holy Church is the guarantor of the Faith. God will honour His Spouse's cheques no matter how badly written or misspelt. Thus the new rites for the Sacraments are valid, although one and all are lamentable productions. They remain cheques drawn by the Church on God's inexhaustible account, in spite of the smudges and blots.

But the Church is not only the guarantor of the Faith, she is also Faith's guardian, and guardian of the faithful. It is in these fields that the present Administration has such a bad record. Has the Faith been guarded? Yes, twice in words: by *Humanae Vitae* and the Credo of the People of God. But by deeds? What heresy has been condemned? Which heretic excommunicated? Why have sound catechisms been withdrawn and unsound ones propagated? How is it that any Eucharist is permitted and alone the Immemorial Mass excluded? One could go on indefinitely.

138

As for the wretched faithful, far from being protected, they have been trampled under foot. Their faith has been derided as totem-worship, their religious practice as tribal custom, their devotions as superstition, their innermost convictions as sentimentality. Only one item in their religion remains unchanged: the collection is still passed round.

It is not unlikely that in your career as a diplomat you have never had cure of souls. If you had, you might be prepared to take more seriously the Church's role as guardian of the faithful. You would not have allowed God's little ones to be scandalized as they have been. It is for God's sake and theirs, not for mine, that

I remain,
In indignant opposition,
E. F.

◇   ◇   ◇

36.   Second letter to Henry Dobson, Bishop of Hunstanton. *(The first is #6.)*
Thursday, February 10th, 1977.

Dear Harry,

I apologise for the delay in answering your letter. The fact is that I have been rather busy. If you find that time weighs heavily on your hands I strongly urge you to permit the old Mass in your diocese. From then onwards you will never have a dull moment.

On Tuesday I was over at Horethorpe Hall. Do you know the place? It used to belong to the Veronican Sisters. I have bought it to start up a seminary. Of course I had been there umpteen times but never before had I explored it nook and cranny. It is not only vast but utterly lovely—the proportions of the rooms, the convenience of the layout, the refinement of the decoration. Actually, it is highly decorated: fireplaces with elaborate overmantles, panels, pilasters, cornices, ceilings—all in stucco—but so perfectly executed as never to be oppressive. Whatever the shortcomings of our ancestors two hundred years ago, they have left us standards of taste which have never been equalled.

Yes, I am opening a seminary. Lefebvre is perfectly right: there is no shortage of vocations provided the aspirants are given a clear vision of what they are called to and for. In fact, now that the Church is in danger, there are probably more than ever before. With the generosity of youth they are eager to defend her. But this means that their vocation is in defence of the old religion. I shall open after Easter with ten students and with another fourteen or more due in September. Alas! I have had to reject nearly as many applicants as I have accepted.

(There follows a paragraph concerning Mgr Bouverie, the Trust and the Institute of St John Fisher.)

The trouble is that I shall not live to ordain more than one of these men. What will my successor do (and I have a shrewd idea who he will be)? He may well ordain them in spite of being no traditionalist because he would otherwise have no students at all. If he refuses to do so, however, I have a guarantee of ordination from a bishop whose name I have promised to keep secret. Nevertheless I should die a much happier man if my students had two strings to their bow. You need not put anything in writing. Your word is good enough. Were I in better shape I should come over and see you but travelling upsets me. I paid for my visit to Horethorpe by spending yesterday in bed. Could you come over to Stamford some time? We could then discuss the whole matter. Apart from anything else, I should be grateful of your advice. I may disagree with you and think you have rum ideas but I do trust you.

Thank you for telling me about poor Charlie Blythe. Do you know that at first he wanted to follow my example? So now he is trying to organize my exclusion from the Episcopal Conference and the Low Week Meeting! I mistrust me of enthusiasts. On the other hand, I have been just as ill-served by my totally unflappable friend, Canon Cocksedge. However, one cannot go through life trusting nobody and I infinitely prefer to be deceived than untrusting.

So much for my news. I now turn to your criticism.

Really, you have the most abstract mind I know. First you attacked me because I was running counter to the "trend of history." You now return to the charge on the ground that I am running against the trend of science. "All living organisms," you write, "are subject to change and the changes in the Church are no more than a proof of its vitality." You add for good measure that "never has the world changed as rapidly and radically as within our lifetime, so it is only natural that the Church should exhibit the same phenomenon."

140

Concerning the latter sentence, I readily admit that you and I have witnessed astonishing technical changes. In my childhood, my mother cooked over an open fire, we drew water from the well, we went to bed by candlelight and to town in a horse-drawn bus—and this not thirty miles from London Bridge. Yes, the harnessing of energy has produced astonishing changes. But these changes all concern the use or accidents of things. They have changed the nature neither of the things nor the users. The moon is the identical moon even though it now bears human footprints. The astronaut is still the identical person although he may have been traumatized by his experience. However, I do not want to get involved in the philosophy of change. The point I wish to make concerns a simple matter of fact. It is this: whereas the uses to which things are put have undergone unparalleled changes, never has there been so little change in the personnel of the users, at least in what was once Christendom. The birthrate has fallen like a plummet and, apart from myself, nobody seems to die. The personnel remains astonishingly constant. The authors of my boyhood, P. G. Wodehouse, Bertrand Russell, Martin D'Arcy, Jacques Maritain, were all still writing in the 1970s. Thus, when you say that "never has the world changed so rapidly and radically as within our lifetime" you are saying something which is less than a half-truth. Moreover, religion deals precisely with the personnel—including the three Persons of the Trinity. It would consequently have been nearer the truth had you said: "Never has the personnel of the world changed so little as in our lifetime, so it is only natural that the Church should exhibit a minimum of change." That would not do at all, would it, Harry? So I shall not press the argument. I shall only say that I find the present situation immensely funny: a few antediluvian youth experts, using aging priests with aging congregations, invent a youth-religion for non-existent youths.

Now let us have a look at your main thesis: "All living organisms are subject to change and the changes in the Church are no more than a proof of its vitality." It is specious enough, but you realize that it is based on a false syllogism? It would be just as illogical to say: all dying organisms exhibit change; the Church exhibits change; therefore the Church is a dying organism. So that won't do.

Surely the trouble is that your view of the universe, logically enough, is identical with your view of history. In history you believe in an irreversible trend called progress. In science you believe in an irreversible trend called evolution. The latter is just as false as the former. There is all the evidence in the world for development and decay but none for evolution. I doubt if there is a serious scientist today who uses the word. He may talk cautiously about mutations but not about evolution. He will even mention that, owing to the second law of thermodynamics, things move towards chaos but not the other way round, since this would imply a new source of energy. If one wants to be up to date, in fact, one ought to talk about devolution.

As far as I know, only two groups of people really believe in evolution: 1. the true heirs of all 19th-century errors, the Marxists; 2. the new churchmen, who have just heard of it from Teilhard de Chardin. This doubtless explains why the new churchmen are Communists: the two groups share a common view of the universe. What really tickles me is that in a few years' time the Church alone in the world will be maintaining the theory of Communism, partly out of conservatism but principally because the clergy always seem to get hold of an idea when it is dead.

As for our immediate concern, the changes in the Church, it is not inconceivable that, after much prayer and fasting, motivated less by learning than by holiness, duly conscious of the enormity of the task and exercising scrupulous care, it is not inconceivable, I admit, that a word or rubric here, a devotional practice there, might be changed for the better. Even then more prayer and fasting would be needed before one could be sure that the change was so great an improvement as to warrant changing the practices of several hundred million Catholics. Quite apart from religion, in any human activity the chances of change for the better are limited and difficult to judge; the chances of change for the worse are limitless and require no judgement at all. Have you invariably changed the diocesan investments for the better?

The very volume of changes in the Church since Vatican II is sufficient to guarantee that most of them are for the worse. It is inconceivable that over the past two thousand years the Church has manifested and expressed the Faith so badly that any and every change must be for the better. If that were so, she would lose all credibility. What is conceivable, on the other hand, is that some of the changes may have been for the better and some not. But this possibility is one which we are not allowed even to discuss. To do so is disloyal, divisive and conducive to schism. Every change is for the better; there has not been the least error, the slightest slip. And this is maintained with a straight face although clauses 7, 48, 55, 56 and 60 of the *Institutio Generalis* of the New Ordo had to be revised within a year of publication. Apparently such cases only go to show how the better can be turned into super and super-plus, like petrol. Anyway, we are not supposed to pick and choose; we must accept the changes in block. Paul VI has expressed the situation perfectly in his allocution of May 24th, 1976: "By the supreme authority which We have received from Christ, We decree the same prompt obedience to all reforms, be they liturgical, disciplinary or pastoral, which of recent years have grown up out of the decrees of the Council." The reason for this is simple: although the changes parade as reforms of this and that, they are not. What they are is the multitudinous manifestation of a single doctrinaire position—which no one in authority has the courage to define. Of course we are all aware of the explanation given for never putting a foot wrong in a thousand changes: "It is the Holy Spirit guides us lest we should chance to trip on a stone." Unfortunately that was, and doubtless still is, the temptation at the pinnacle of the Temple in the Holy City. And we know the answer: "Thou shalt not tempt the Lord thy God."

No, my dear Harry, neither in theory nor in practice can I accept your views of change. Of course all finite things change. God alone is changeless. But the closer to God the less change there is. We ourselves shall be changeless when we come to rest in the Beatific Vision. It is Hell which is perpetual motion. The Church is a divine institution and this is made most manifest by her changelessness. Those who dare to change her are masking her identity.

◇   ◇   ◇

On Friday Bishop Forester wrote individually to each of the five clerical students of the diocese. He had not written to them since his collective letter of January 20th (#17). The letter to Mr Parker and an extract from that to Mr Baldock will be sufficient to give the tenor of the others.

37.   To the Reverend John Parker,
           Theological College, London.
Friday, February 11th, 1977.

Dear Mr Parker,

You have doubtless seen in the press that I am not expected to live long. This is true and it has reminded me that there is some urgency in restoring order in the diocese and provision must be made for continuity after my death.

Concerning urgency. I said that I would ordain you on May 28th. I shall bring the date forward to Easter Sunday, April 10th, at 10:30 a.m. here in the Cathedral. Your pre-ordination retreat will start on Saturday evening, April 2nd. It will be conducted by Mgr Charles Bouverie at Horethorpe Hall, near Horebury. You probably know the place.

Concerning provision for the future. Horethorpe Hall has been bought from the Veronican Sisters by a Trust devoted to the maintenance of religious sanity. It will therefore not be dependent on my successor. After your ordination and Easter holiday, you will not return to the Theological College but to Horethorpe, which is to become a seminary of which Mgr Bouverie will be Rector. In future all students at Horethorpe will have to join the Institute of St John Fisher, concerning which I enclose some literature. This, of course, does not apply to you or the other existing students since I accepted you for the diocese before the Institute was founded. I hope you will join it but shall exert no pressure on you. The Institute is reasonably safe: in the first week twenty-two priests have joined it.

After Easter there will be eleven students at Horethorpe including yourself: the five existing diocesan students, five ex-seminarians and a convert clergyman. The number is likely to double after September. It does not directly concern you but it may interest you to know that the ordination of members of the Institute is guaranteed after my death.

There, my dear Mr Parker, so much for that. Incidentally, I am writing along the same lines to Mr Evans and have already informed your Rector that you and Evans will be leaving at the end of this term.

You can have little idea how much I look forward to ordaining you. It is a wonderful thing to see a young man willing to sacrifice his life in order to offer the Sacrifice of

God Incarnate. That and nothing else is what the priesthood is. Of course God is not mean and will repay you a thousand-fold, as I know full well from my own experience. But—and this also I know from experience—He will repay your sacrifice only in the measure that you acknowledge His. There is no joy even remotely equivalent to that of a priest at the altar of God. It is beyond all expression. But it all depends on sacrifice for Sacrifice. If either goes there is a void which nothing can fill. For seven years I compromised with the world and my side of the sacrifice was somehow impure, equivocal. My cancer is no more than the physical expression of my spiritual turmoil. But by God's grace I again stand erect and clean before His altar. He has repaid me with compound interest for the wasted years. On my death certificate cancer will doubtless be inscribed as the cause of death but in fact I shall have died of joy.

◊　◊　◊

38.　　Extract from a letter to Mr Geoffrey Baldock,
　　　　St Wilfred's Seminary, York.
Friday, February 11th, 1977.

(Most of the letter is similar to that to Mr Parker.)
　... Since you are to be ordained subdeacon, I wish to add a personal note on priestly celibacy. You see, we priests receive so much. Far more obviously than any layman, we are at the receiving end of God's bounty. The service of God provides our livelihood and security. We receive kindness and respect from those around us because we are God's priests. As though this were not enough, God showers grace and mercy on us in the measure that we are humble and holy. To receive so much so constantly produces its own problem. How can we tell that our love of God is disinterested, that we love Him for His sake and not for the benefits we receive for our service? How can I, Edmund Forester, console myself against the thought that I am a mere hireling and no true son? So much have I received! Well, I have made a sacrifice of the most fundamental urge I have. Also, it was not a sacrifice once made at my subdeaconate and then finished. It has had to be preserved every day of my priestly life. It is in this respect, in its constancy, that no other human sacrifice

can compare with celibacy and virginity. Its primary purpose is to honour God, so that we who stand at the altar of His Sacrifice shall have made the most fundamental sacrifice we can. But its secondary use is to prove our good faith, not to others but to ourselves. As a matter of fact others will not call your good faith in question no matter how much they disagree with you. Even today the loyalty of the faithful to their priests is almost pathetic. Inevitably, however, you will doubt yourself. This is not easy to bear. It is then that you can remember your vow of celibacy. You have made a sacrifice. You have made a gesture which is totally disinterested. And you continue to make it every day of your life. Whatever your failings, at least you serve Him for His sake.

CHAPTER VI

PENANCE

Bishop Forester wrote to me as usual over the week-end, on Saturday, February 12th. It is a relaxed letter about the antics of Mr Glauben's photographer and his visit to Horethorpe. Apart from the letters to the seminarians he had written a fourth Ad clerum *to accompany a Pastoral Letter which was already in print and was to be read on the following Sunday, Quinquagesima.*

39.   To the Clergy of Stamford Diocese.
    Ad clerum 77-4
Monday, February 14th, 1977.

Right Reverend, Very Reverend and Reverend Fathers,

1. I first wish to thank you for your support since my *Ad clerum* of January 13th, only a month ago. It seems to have reunited your parishes and given your people a sense of cohesion and direction. This is what I had hoped but it would have been impossible without your collaboration. I am also deeply grateful to the twenty-three priests who have already notified Mgr Defew of their willingness to join the Institute of St John Fisher.

2. Herewith a Pastoral Letter to be read at all Masses next Sunday, February 20th, being Quinquagesima in the old calendar. It deals with Confession. I earnestly hope that you will follow it up during the first three Sundays of Lent by preaching on what I have omitted, notably on the principal sins, how to examine one's conscience and what is meant by contrition.

3. Concerning Confession: a) please impose a penance such that the penitent knows when he has fulfilled it. Such penances as "Do a good deed" or "Put what you can in the poor-box" can only lead to scruples since what is "good" and "what one can" are not specified; b) I see no reason for the change in the prayers of absolution; it is change for its own sake. The old prayers should consequently be used. They may, however, be said in the vernacular except for the one containing the form of absolution which should be said in Latin.

4. Ash Wednesday and all Fridays in Lent will be days of fasting and abstinence.

5. The Stations of the Cross are to be recited in Parish Churches on all Fridays in Lent and followed (except on Good Friday) by Benediction in reparation for the outrages committed against God's law.

6. The Holy Week ceremonies in the Cathedral will be celebrated according to the revised rite of Pius XII. I trust that the example will be followed by all other churches in the diocese. The ceremonies of the Easter Vigil should not start before 10:30 p.m. on Saturday night.

7. On Maundy Thursday I shall celebrate the Mass of the Holy Oils at 10 a.m. in the Cathedral. I shall bless the Oil of Catechumens as well as that for the Sick and Holy Chrism. Deanery representatives should therefore bring three recipients for the Holy Oils as of yore.

8. At 10:30 a.m. on Easter Sunday in the Cathedral I shall ordain the Reverends John Parker to the priesthood, Michael Evans to the diaconate, Geoffrey Baldock to the subdiaconate; I shall give the tonsure and First Minors to Messrs Henry Carr and Richard Thwaites. Please ask

148

your people to thank God for their vocations and pray for their perseverance.

9. As you have doubtless heard, Horethorpe Hall is to become a seminary. It will open after Easter with eleven students.

10. Since the Oil of Catechumens will be available, from Easter Sunday onwards Baptism may be administered according to the traditional rite. The prayers may be said in the vernacular with the exception of: a) the formal exorcism and the *Ephpheta* which follows it; b) the *Ego te lineo oleo salutis*; c) the form of Baptism; d) the prayer *Deus omnipotens* which accompanies the anointing with Chrism.

11. Also from Easter Sunday onwards the Sacrament of Extreme Unction may be administered according to the traditional rite. The prayer following the *Confiteor* and the anointings should be said in Latin but the rest may be said in English.

12. I am completely reorganizing the Diocesan Schools' Commission. Fr Daly has relinquished the secretaryship and his place will be taken by Dean Nial McCarthy, whom I have also made an Honorary Canon. The Commission will have three sub-committees: a) Religious Instruction headed by Mgr Bouverie, Rector of Horethorpe Seminary; this will deal with the syllabus and textbooks used in Catholic schools; b) Governors, headed by Mr Edward Outman of 5 Exchange Buildings, Sandborough; this will advise on the appointment and duties of all lay Governors and Managers; c) Finance, headed by Canon McCarthy. During the course of next term all schools will be visited by a member of the Commission apart from the usual School Inspectors. Mr Outman would be grateful if the secretary of all Governing Bodies would notify him of their meetings so that he or his delegate can attend.

I am well aware that Parish Priests are deeply worried about their schools: declining numbers, inadequate and non-Catholic staff, uncertainty in the matter and method of instruction. What was once your pride has become your burden. One cannot expect a miracle from the new Commission but at least it will take your problems seriously, give you authoritative guidance and relieve you of some of the responsibility. I can only apologize for having allowed the present state of affairs to have dragged on for so long.

13. Although it concerns the subject of the Pastoral, I have left till last the question of Penitential Services. I have seen these very well done here in the diocese. They gave instruction on sin, motives for contrition and encouragement to have recourse to sacramental absolution. In no way did they pretend to be a substitute for Confession. This, however, is not what the initiators of Penitential Services intended. For them it was the thin end of a wedge—or rather a tin-opener to get the faithful out of the confessional box. It is a question of "obrogation." Just as a community Communion Service has been substituted for the Sacrifice of the Mass, so should a Penetential Service with community absolution replace auricular confession. Indeed this has already happened in France, as I noticed when I was there last September. No times for Confession were advertised in church porches but only the times of Penitential Services. Priests even refuse to hear confessions. Such is the danger and it is a very real one. I wish the whole problem to be discussed at Deanery meetings in due course. In the meantime I lay down the following rules for Penitential Services in the diocese:

a) there must be at least two priests present: one to conduct the service while the other or others hear sacramental Confession;

b) the Service must contain nothing which might lead the faithful to imagine that they have received absolution;

c) the Service may not be held more than once a month in the same parish;

d) auricular Confession must be available and advertised at the usual times.

In fact, Penitential Services are to be encouraged if they lead to the Sacrament of Penance but must not be allowed to become a substitute for it.

◇ ◇ ◇

40.   A Pastoral Letter.
Monday, February 14th, 1977.

Edmund, by the Grace of God and favour of the Apostolic See, Bishop of Stamford to the Clergy secular and regular and to the Faithful of the said Diocese, health and benediction in the Lord.

Dearly beloved Brethren in Jesus Christ,

Fortunately there are few people in the world who believe that they alone are always right and everyone else always wrong, that they alone are always good and everyone else invariably wicked. We know exactly where they are, these unfortunate people who think themselves perfect: they are in lunatic asylums. It is a strange phenomenon that the human being, the summit of the visible creation, should be universally conscious of his own imperfection. Indeed, the saner he is the more he is aware of his liability to err; the better he is the more he is aware of his liability to sin. If you think that you are sometimes wrong it is proof that you have right judgement. If you think that you sometimes sin it is proof that you have a sound conscience. It is precisely to remedy this state of affairs that God has revealed what we must believe for our salvation, so that we may have certainty in so vital a matter. As for what we must do for our salvation, He has not only revealed how we should act but has given us a means by which we are put right when we go wrong. This is the subject of my Pastoral Letter: Confession and the forgiveness of sin.

I

Before embarking on forgiveness I should like to say a few words about sin. Sin, as you remember from your catechism, is the deliberate disobedience of the known commandments of God. These commandments, summed up in the Ten Commandments and interpreted by Holy Church,

151

constitute the Natural Law. The Natural Law is not what human beings happen to do but what God requires them to do. A sin, therefore, is an objective act which a human performs, be it interiorly in his mind or exteriorly in his deeds. Our subjective conscience, in fact, has little or nothing to do with sin. If we are lucky it may tell us that we have sinned but it does not necessarily tell us what is sinful. The people who obey most perfectly their consciences are clearly those who have none; people with a delicate conscience are constantly disobeying it. Thus it comes about that saints think of themselves as sinners whereas crooks think of themselves as saints. This we know from our own experience. Have you ever met a rogue who is not self-satisfied or a noble character who is?

If sin has little to do with our conscience, it has even less to do with the feeling of shame. We may be delighted at getting away with a thumping lie and thoroughly ashamed at being incorrectly dressed. We may feel no shame at stealing an article from a self-service store but overwhelmed with it when we are caught. Besides, shame is not equally attached to all sins. Nobody feels ashamed at not saying his prayers but may be desperately so for a sexual act done scarcely deliberately and with doubtful consent.

Then again, sin is an offence against God. It must not be confused with crime, which is an offence against the State or community. Crime and sin may coincide, as is the case in certain forms of murder, but not always. Thus the State encourages and pays for abortion, the murder of the totally innocent and totally defenceless: the most sinful form of murder is counted a social virtue. Adultery is a sin but not a crime. On the other hand, avoiding certain forms of taxation, notably death duties, may be a crime but is not a sin. You can get into endless trouble for breaking a traffic regulation without any spot on your soul. This is more important than it may seem for two reasons. Firstly, Catholics can be tempted to fall in with the standards of the society around them. They may be led to believe that what is not a crime cannot be a very grave sin. Oh yes it can! Secondly, some Catholics today seem to imagine that sin is an offence against the community. It is true that we act wrongly rather often against our neighbour, but our neighbour is a person, not a community, and the sinfulness of the action comes about because it offends God. Moreover such grave sins as the hatred of God, internal pride and envy may not affect the community in any way. In fact, we Catholics must maintain at all costs the supremacy and independence of God's moral law as against the penal law of the State and the conventions of the community.

So much for the nature of sin.

II

Since all human beings realize that they are imperfect and all good ones know they sin, what can they do about it? The situation of upright, holy people outside the Church is very sad: they know they sin and are too honest to imagine that they can forgive themselves. No matter how hopefully they may trust in God's mercy, they are obliged to carry the burden of their sins around with them for as long as they live. I have often wondered if this is not why some of the finest non-Catholics I have met tended to be rather sad and serious. Anyway, beyond a doubt, it is to have the certainty of forgiveness that a number of splendid converts have come into the Church.

But the majority of human beings are not as heroic as all that. So what do they do? They can deny that sin exists, with what dire consequences we know only too well. They can attempt to bury their sins by forgetting them; but it does not always work. The overwhelming majority simply justify themselves, as did our First Parents. You remember the account of the Fall and how Adam reacted when faced with the first sin: "The woman whom thou gavest me to be my companion, she it was who offered me fruit from the tree." Eve likewise: "The serpent," she said, "beguiled me." It is exactly the same today, in spite of the vaunted change in the modern world. Clearly the easiest way to justify oneself is to blame somebody else. Adam had no choice: it was Eve's fault. Eve at least had the decency not to accuse Adam and so start the first family row. You will notice, too, how Adam indirectly blames God: "the woman whom thou gavest me," so it is really all God's fault. How typical! As it was in the beginning, is now and ever shall be.

Just think for a moment of the hundreds of millions of people around us. They are not all wicked by any means, yet all sin, and the overwhelming majority promptly justify

153

themselves. It is at this point that the sublimity of our holy religion becomes manifest:

Instead of denying the existence of sin, we define it most carefully;

Instead of burying the memory of sin, we recall it to mind by examining our conscience;

Instead of justifying ourselves, we accuse ourselves;

Instead of carrying the burden of sin around with us, we have the certainty of forgiveness.

This is all so wonderful, so splendid and so unnatural that it is clearly divine.

Dearly beloved Brethren, we Catholics are no better than our neighbours, indeed we are often much worse, but we are different. In the whole wide world we are the only group of people who deliberately set out to accuse ourselves. It is neither an agreeable nor an easy process. We do it as best we can, which is usually rather badly. That does not matter. God clearly knows our sins infinitely better than we do and we do not pretend to supply Him with news. What He wants from us is the humility to attempt self-accusation. And it must be real, not just in our minds: that is why He demands that it be made with the representative of His Church, the priest, as judge and witness. If we have the humility to accuse ourselves, He will not accuse us at the Judgement. Yes, it is for humility that God searches our hearts and He will not look in vain in the hearts of those who confess, whereas the upright who do not are so often kept erect by pride.

III

Now, in the revolution through which the Church is passing there is a victim which has suffered even more than the Mass. It is Confession, the Sacrament of Penance. The revolution claims to be a "renewal." From the dawn of history there have been renewals and revivals. All have had the same message in a thousand forms: "Repent and do penance! God may yet relent and forgive." The present renewal is unique: instead of repentance, permissiveness is preached, the Sacrament of Penance is neglected and the confessionals abandoned. When doom is threatening the Western world more surely than it did Nineveh in the days of Jonas, there is none

154

to cry out "Repent and do penance! God may yet relent and forgive."

This is an unmitigated disaster. Even in our diocese the decline in Easter confessions has far outstripped the fall in Mass attendance. Have you lost the notion of sin as an offence against God? Do you believe it to be a matter for your own conscience? Are you incapable of the humility needed for self-accusation? Do you imagine that you can forgive yourselves? No, probably not. You have merely allowed yourselves to be carried along by the revolutionary process. You have strayed like sheep without a shepherd. Alas! It is I, under Christ, who am your shepherd. Too late, perhaps, when my voice is feeble and the sheep beyond recall, too late I cry: "Repent and do penance! God may yet relent and forgive."

Next Wednesday is Ash Wednesday. Easter Duties must be fulfilled between then and Trinity Sunday, June 5th. The obligation is to Holy Communion. But what about confession? Dare I admit that I am terrified of sacrilegious Communions? In this diocese I have seen large numbers of communicants in parishes where the priests assure me that confessions are few. I am forced to believe that your consciences are clear but is it because you have ceased to examine them? I wish to remind you that Our Lord was more concerned over His sacramental than His physical body. He prayed for those who crucified Him: "Father, forgive them for they know not what they do." Of Judas He said: "It were better had he never been born." And what had Judas done? At the Last Supper he had received Communion unworthily: "The morsel once given, Satan entered into him." The difference is that Judas, unlike the soldiers but like us, knew what he was doing. Thus, the more frequent your Communions, the more frequent should be your confessions.

It is clear enough that one of the reasons for the sharp rise in the number of communicants is the abolition of the Eucharistic fast. There is now no barrier other than sin to receiving Our Lord. Hence there is automatic social pressure in favour of receiving. The person who does not either lacks piety or is in a state of sin. No such presumption was possible when there was the barrier of fasting: those who did not receive had merely broken their fast and those who received had prepared themselves by keeping it. In fact the abolition of the Eucharistic fast, especially for children and youths, can be the cause of exerting unbearable pressure in favour of sacrilegious Communions. And the habit once contracted will not easily be broken. One is sometimes forced to wonder whether those who stay in their pews are not more devout than those who approach the altar. I think people would be well advised this Lent to make a private resolution to Our Lord to keep a three hour Eucharistic fast. It might help you and your children to resist the social pressure in favour of unworthy Communions.

Alas! The pressure has not only been social but also religious. If the Mass is a meal and not a sacrifice, there is no point in going unless you eat; and those who do turn up are expected to share the meal. No attention is paid to the terrible parable of the wedding feast in which the guest improperly prepared, without a wedding garment, is damned: "Bind him hand and foot and cast him out into the darkness where there shall be weeping and gnashing of teeth." However, our obligation is to attend the Sacrifice of God Incarnate in the Mass. Apart from Easter Duties, you are under no obligation to partake in any sacred meal.

Lent is now upon you. "Here is the time of pardon; here is the day of salvation." Without the Sacrament of Penance your penances are worthless. Your sacrifices will be useless if offered with unclean hands. Your Communions will be sacrilegious without pure hearts. "Turn the whole bent of your hearts back to God. It is your hearts that must be torn asunder. Come back to Him for He is ever gracious and merciful, ever patient and rich in pardon."

Repent and do penance! God may yet relent and forgive. Given at Stamford etc.

◇　◇　◇

41.　Second letter to the Reverend Giles Pocock, Parish Priest of Blackwater.
(The first is # 11.)
Wednesday, February 16th, 1977.

Dear Father Pocock,

I am flattered that you should think my *Ad clerum* no. 3 impressive—although, of course, you have reservations and regret its amateur approach. The trouble is that you professionals keep prudent silence, so it is left to us amateurs to do as best we can. I wonder how far prudence is a virtue? As long as it pays or as long as it does not pay, which? With my usual imprudence, I plumb for the latter. Anyway, why do you not while away your leisure hours by translating my amateur efforts into professional terms? It would carry a lot of weight, coming from you.

I notice that you take particular exception to my remark that the irregularities in the Constitution of 1969 should "make me highly suspicious of the present administration." "What," you ask, "do you mean by 'present administration?' Are you referring to the Pope, the Secretary of State, the Papal entourage, the bishops, to whom?" Curiously enough, I mean what I say; I am referring to the present administration, which in varying degrees involves both the Pope and his entourage.

Let us suppose that you applied the same sentence to the diocese of Stamford, what would you mean? You would mean that the diocese was badly run, that there seemed to be a great muddle at the top, that when the bishop said one thing his executives promptly did the opposite, that pressure groups made the appointments with jobs for the lads and that the only person who thought that everything was going splendidly was Edmund Forester himself. That is the sort of moan you would make—and surely you would have every right to do so. As a matter of fact it has not been all that untrue in my particular case. However, the point I am getting at is that you could not exonerate me from the muddle in Stamford. I may not have been the author of a particular bungle but I remain responsible, more especially as it is I who choose my entourage and appoint my executives. Exactly the same applies to Paul VI: he may not be the author of all the muddle but he is reponsible for it.

Do you remember the wonderful remark of Maréchal Foch after the 1914-18 war? A bevy of French generals wrote their memoirs in which each claimed to have won the Battle of the Marne. Somebody asked the Commander-in-Chief whom he thought had won it. Foch replied: *"Je ne sais pas qui l'a gagnée mais je sais qui l'aurait perdue"*—I don't know who won it but I know who would have been held responsible for losing it. Exactly!

I realize that the motive of your objection is that you wish to exonerate the Pope and put the blame partly on his entourage but principally on the bishops. This position

157

seemed perfectly tenable during and immediately after the Council; let us say for the first five years of his reign, until 1968. But it is quite untenable now. No Pope in history has gone to such lengths to ensure an entourage and episcopate of his own choosing as Paul VI. The Cardinals lose the power to vote at the age of eighty so that only those of his own making will be able to vote for his successor. Bishops are made to retire at seventy-five so that the overwhelming majority of the episcopate is of his own appointment. Everything is his own, from the Mass he says to the bishops who say it. Incidentally, never in the history of the Church has the appointment of bishops been so absolutely dependent upon Rome. Of old, Concordats or custom allowed some interference from the State so that the Vatican was not always to blame. Today, it is only in Communist countries that interference is permitted. The result has been the appointment of eminently worthy bureaucrats unsuited to command. Hence the lack of independence among the bishops. There is not the personnel to offer opposition. Actually, my dear Father, if in the administration you try to divide the head from the members, it is the members which you will exonerate. I am more charitable to Paul VI than you.

I should like to add a humble word in defence of us bishops. We are ground between the upper and nether millstones of the administration and the faithful. The faithful refuse to move and the administration to stop moving. I need not expatiate on the faithful as I know that their immobility exasperates you. Concerning the administration, just have a look at the bumf churned out in the *Acta* alone, quite apart from sheaves of other notifications, communications, rectifications, ramifications, rumifications; and these besides umpteen conferences and committees each producing resolutions, irresolutions and confusions. Small wonder most bishops have given up reading and watch television instead! You know, one can judge the competence of any government by the number of laws it makes. A good one will administer the laws at its disposal with the minimum of fuss and change. A bad one will constantly be legislating and throwing the administration out of gear. This is as true of civil as of ecclesiastical government. England is in chaos because of the mass production of laws. Our monetary inflation is the financial expression of our legislative inflation. It is exactly the same with the Church. It is in chaos because the proliferation of legislation has choked the administration. There is a fine lot of "-ations" for you: I must be a deep thinker.

Yes, I feel desperately sorry for my colleagues. The older ones came back from their Council full of conscious pride. They had left their mark on Holy Church. Their names were immortalized on marble slabs in the porch of St Peter's. What happened? Too soon they were seventy-five. They were put out to grass. A grazing bishop is a sorry sight. Then came their successors with hopes high and illusions untrammelled by experience. I need not describe their disillusion as the millstones ground them down. Most pathetic is that here are thoroughly good men who have arrived at the pinnacle of their ambition. They themselves have become what in all the world they reverence most: a bishop of Holy Church. They find themselves helpless, hopeless and despised. I know, my dear Father, because that was my position until a month ago. It is tragic. But, you will say, it is all their own fault and they know it. Yes, and that makes the situation the less bearable.

You ask me what I think of the present Holy Father. I fail to see how "what I think" enters the question. He may be a saint but an impossible Pope, as was Celestine V. He may be a sinner but a good Pope, as was Alexander VI. Whatever he is, saint or sinner, the reign of Paul VI bids fair to being the most disastrous in the history of the Church. Moreover, he must bear the responsibility for it in the judgement of men although he may bear little in the judgement of God.

All that is rather sad and serious, so I shall end on a lighter note. It is a parody of the quip against Charles II— "Here comes His Majesty the King. . . ." Alas! I cannot claim authorship:

An Epitaph

Here lies His Holiness Pope Paul
Who never faced the facts:
No folly in his words at all,
Nor wisdom in his acts.

P.S. I am delighted to hear that the Duchess has attended the parish church. She has held out the olive branch. Perhaps you could do likewise by saying the Immemorial Mass on one Sunday a month.

◇ ◇ ◇

42.   To the Reverend Bryan Houghton,
Avignon, France.
Sunday, February 20th, 1977.

Dear Bryan,

I knew it would happen. I received a notice from the Delegation on Thursday and it was in the press yesterday. Klushko has been appointed Secretary to the Congregation for Bishops and Testastorta will succeed him as Apostolic Delegate to Great Britain. Testa has already gone to Rome to be consecrated bishop. I doubt if it will change the situation as far as I am concerned. Klushko will continue to manufacture the ammunition which the wretched Testa will have to fire. For the first few months Testa will be as happy as a sandboy but inevitably some of the ammunition will go off in his hand.

On Friday I had a visit from Glauben. He brought his wife. They came by helicopter. She is a charming young woman, a French Jewess from Carpentras in your part of the world. She has heard of your existence and will get in touch with you when she visits her people in September.

Glauben brought me proofs of advertisements for his great campaign. He is as pleased as punch with them. They are absolutely frightful. The bejewelled beetle is snarling and wagging his gloved finger in reproof at the reader. The text varies according to the seaminess of the paper. The general line is: "What's he saying? He says you're lousy and will go to Hell. Who is he? The R.C. Bishop of Stamford, who tells the truth. What's he doing? Dying of cancer. What does he want? Lots of money to carry on his good work. Send your cheques to the Dowager Duchess of Blackwater. . . ." The advertisements for the women's papers are exactly the opposite. The Duchess looks absolutely tremendous wearing her coronet and dripping with pearls. The text is a message about handing on the lamp of Christian teaching to the kiddies. "You see," Glauben explained, "men love being thought wicked even if they are as respectable as a bowler hat. It gives them a feeling of importance and independence. They don't go to church because the clergy no longer tell them what a lousy lot they are. So your advertisement will go into papers for men, opposite the pin-up page. It will be worth a couple of hundred thousand at least. With women, of course, it's the other way round. They like to be told how good they are even if they're worth less than their bikinis. So the Duchess will go into all the women's papers. She's tremendous. I couldn't put a top figure as to what she's worth.

"Of course the whole campaign is an absolute gift. To have a real, live Duchess appealing for a bishop who talks about Hell and is dying of cancer will strike a chord in every British heart. The first ones will appear next Thursday: you in *British Beauties* and the Duchess in *Ladies' Leisure* and they'll go on until I've covered the lot."

"But I don't talk about Hell," I expostulated.

"Perhaps not, but you believe in it."

"How do you know?"

"You don't think I'm so careless as to write that highly confidential letter without discovering the sort of man you are? I immediately got my research department on to you. When you were at Grumby you used to publish a monthly article in the local rag. I liked your story on Hell. Wait a minute, I've got a copy of it in the briefcase."

Indeed he had. It is rather blush-making to read what one wrote over twenty years ago. It is a variation on a tale by Villiers de l'Isle-Adam. I enclose it.

"Anyway," I continued, "you won't put that sort of stuff in the *Times* or *Guardian*, I trust."

"Good heavens, no! I won't bother about them. There's no money there. You see, owing to the incidence of taxation and the addition of social benefits, a working man with wife and three dependent children earning £50 a week has more spare money than an executive with the same family earning £8,000 a year. Indeed, if the executive is trying to educate his children privately, he will be heavily in debt and have mort-gaged his future. No, the serious papers are no use. It's the people who can afford the glossies who have got the money. Also the readers of specialized papers—gardening, cooking, foreign travel, the arts, antiques. Here's one for foreign travel: 'Where are you going for your holidays? To Hell, says the Bishop.'" And so on.

I have not laughed so much in a decade. I suppose it is all right. Anyway, he is putting up the money. Apparently among his many interests he has an advertising company. The receipts, incidentally, are graded according to the size of the donation: £1 to £10 normal; £10 to £100 a postcard of the Duchess with the text engraved; £100 to £500 a framed cabinet photograph with her arms embossed; over £500 the same autographed. He advertises for a couple of the brewers and thinks there will be no difficulty in organizing a campaign for "A Duchess in every Pub." I do not know how Her Grace will take to that. However, Glauben will get round her.

What an astonishing fellow he is! When he had finished talking about his advertisements he branched off into Jewish mysticism. It is a subject on which I know exactly nothing. He gave me long quotations—by heart—from a Rabbi Bloch who lived in Cracow at the start of the last century. He has promised to send me a book on them.

There was a Chapter meeting on Thursday. Socks was present. After the meeting the Canons come in for drinks and a chat. Socks behaved as though nothing had happened. He called me Edmund and even asked whether I had heard from Daly. I said that he was still at Deepdale. He then said: "You know, Edmund, Daly was really quite right. It was about time the Stag group was broken up." An extraordinary man! Now that Testa is the Delegate he is practically bound to be my successor.

My Lenten penance will be touring the Convents. Do you know that in this small diocese there are no fewer than thirty-four, including the ex-Veronicans? Up to 1966 there were well over three hundred nuns in them. The numbers have fallen but there are still about three hundred. There are more nuns than secular and regular clergy combined. . . .

(The rest of the letter deals with Bishop Forester's deep misgivings concerning the reaction of the nuns.)

◇   ◇   ◇

43.   *The article to which Mr Glauben referred was published in the* Grumby Clarion *for November 26th, 1955.*

ROMAN CATHOLIC CHURCH NOTES

Our great moral essayist, Dr Samuel Johnson, used to diversify his articles in the *Rambler* with short stories. I propose to do the same. Here is an unpleasant tale called

The Terrible Secret.

He did not look all that old as he lay propped up on his pillows. The plastic surgeons had kept his image much the same over the fifty years that he had been World President.

His vitality had been quite phenomenal up to the previous day. Of course, at diverse times he had been given a new liver, fresh kidneys, a heart transplant as his own organs tended to wear out. But now the doctors were at a loss. The unimaginable seemed inevitable: he was going to die.

His public life had been a fearless battle for progress. It had started over a hundred years ago in a modest way with free abortion on the National Health. As success crowned his efforts, he was emboldened to sponsor euthanasia of the unfit, compulsory abortion of unplanned births, sterilization of persons convicted in the People's Courts for anti-social tendencies and finally the rational system we enjoy today of universal sterilization apart from licensed breeders scientifically selected. With these and similar causes his name will be associated to the end of time.

It was a fitting reward for such services to humanity that he should be elected the first World President.

The most memorable measure of his long tenure of office was, of course, the rationalization of the old, untidy world by planned nuclear explosion, thus giving us the Second Paradise in which we live.

The achievement of which he himself was perhaps most proud was the unification of the world's jarring religions. "Religious freedom," he used to say, "is the basis of democracy. We all adore the same God and are going the same way. All religions are equally right. It is therefore indictable in the People's Courts for anyone to practice or propagate any religion whatsoever. I have come to bring peace, not the sword." It is true that a few fanatics escaped into the Old World Nature Reserve on Land Mass Three, where they are reported still to be arguing and performing their superstitious practices. With the charity which characterized him, the President let them be. They appear, however, to reproduce at a rate which endangers the natural ecology of the Reserve so that the keepers have to thin them out from time to time.

He was entirely devoted to public welfare and seems to have had no private life. His only intimate friend was Mr J.

Iscariot, who was with him as he lay dying. With great effort the President spoke: "There is a terrible secret which must not die with me.... How I know is beyond expression.... But I know it for certain." There was a long pause. "Can you hear me properly? Good! You will be my successor. You too must know. Never divulge it until you are stricken like me. If the people found out all our work would collapse. It is the secret of the world."

The President was sinking fast. Perhaps it was too late; the secret would die with him. Then, with a supreme effort, his noble features distorted with hate, he shrieked in a paroxysm of rage: "Hell exists!"

CHAPTER VII

THE NUNS

Between Monday, February 21st and Saturday, April 2nd, Bishop Forester wrote no fewer than thirty-seven letters of varying length and importance to nuns. There is also a copy-book of his talks to them. These he gave on the Wednesday and Saturday of each week. He would arrive at the convent at 9:30 a.m. to give his first talk. He then interviewed the nuns personally as far as possible and gave a second talk at 12 noon. After lunch he moved on to another convent where he repeated the process, giving his first talk at 3 and his second at 6 p.m. In his condition the effort was heroic.

At each convent his first talk was usually the same. It is a long and carefully written discourse on prayer, of which I shall give important extracts. The second talk varied according to the reaction of his audience. Some are in the form of notes.

It is out of the question to publish this mass of material. Moreover, most of the letters deal with personal problems concerning the spiritual life and are too detailed to be of general interest. They also tend to be repetitive. I shall attempt to give some idea of Bishop Forester's action and the nuns' reaction by quotations from both sources, letters and talks, but principally from the latter.

◇   ◇   ◇

44.   A First Talk: Nuns and Prayer.

One of the most astonishing social phenomena in the first half of this century was the spread of convents. Sociologists, of course, have never noticed it. The immediate reaction to women's emancipation was for them to rush into convents. Admittedly we received the overflow from Ireland and France, but the fact remains that even in Protestant England there is scarcely a township of ten thousand inhabitants without its convent. There are now twice as many nuns in the country as there are priests, whereas in the Age of Faith, in the 15th century, priests outnumbered nuns by about ten to one. My miserable little parish of Grumby, with some five thousand inhabitants of whom about seven hundred were Catholics, could boast two convents with over twenty nuns. And they were my boast, too. I was no more devout than the Methodist Minister and less respected than the Rector, but I could show what they could not: dedicated virgins whose integrity of body expressed their integrity of soul. . . .

The difference between contemplative and active nuns is not as great in reality as appears to outsiders. For both the prime object is the adoration of God. It is only your work which differs. Contemplatives, apart from the liturgy, dig their gardens, print, concoct elixirs or make toothpicks, whereas the active educate children, nurse and care for a thousand human needs. In fact, the work of contemplatives is with things and the work of active nuns with people. Admittedly people are desperately distracting while things are conducive to concentration; nevertheless the object of both is the same: union with God through prayer. . . .

It is nonsense to ascribe the astonishing spread of Catholicism between 1850 and 1960, on the human side, to the clergy. It is due to the nuns. It is you who broke down anti-Catholic prejudice by educating a notable percentage of non-Catholics. It is you who stormed heaven with your prayers and showed men the reality of sanctity. That, indeed, is why you were the revolution's first target: you prayed and educated the future generation of mothers. . . .

In the assault on the institutional Church, her dogmas, the Mass and the sacraments could all be undermined by attacking her priests, questioning their certainties, their function, their authority. Yet that was not enough. It was imperative to dry up her source of prayer. Now, just as priests are the ministers of the Mass so are you nuns the ministers of prayer. And how wonderfully you did it! Well, you must stop immediately. You must get out into the world to "do good" or attend a conference. . . .

It is high time that I said something about prayer. St Thomas places it under the general heading of justice: "to render to God the honour which is his due (*S.T.* 2-2, 81-2)." Prayer is therefore a "natural" virtue and not a specific gift of the Holy Ghost. But Aquinas is talking about prayer in general, the prayer of Jew, Muslim, Hindu, pagan. He is not dealing with the mechanism by which we pray nor with the specific nature of Christian prayer.

Grace, as you know, perfects nature. Thus the natural act of justice in the pagan's prayer is lifted by grace to become a supernatural act of piety by the operation of the Holy Ghost. That is to say that the prayer of a Christian differs from the equivalent act in a pagan not merely by its content or object but in its essence. Whereas the pagan is performing a natural act, aided and abetted by actual grace, the Christian is aiding and abetting a supernatural act performed by the Holy Ghost. The two processes are in fact contrary: the former is a human act sanctified, the latter a divine act humanized.

It is of course true that the Christian must do all in his power to be in a state of grace. Hence the importance attached to what the ancients called "temperance," later writers "mortification" and the moderns "ascetics"; that is, the practice of the virtues and purification of the mind by pious meditation. But the practice of ascetics is not of itself formally prayer. What it does is to provide the circumstance in which prayer is normally possible. It is true that a meditation may be a prayer, but it will be so not by the thing thought but by the intention, since human cooperation with the Holy Ghost is not an act of the intelligence but an act of the will.

Thus the thoughts which a priest expresses in a sermon or a professor of theology in a lecture are not prayers. They remain exactly what they pretend to be: true and pious thoughts. A preacher may indeed move himself to prayer by his own sermon, but as soon as he does so the sermon will grind to a halt. The activity of the human being in prayer is something quite different: it is adherence to grace and the less he impinges on the Holy Ghost the better. This we do not by pious thoughts and good resolutions, which would remain "our" thoughts and "our" resolutions—all forms of self-centeredness—but by here and now being self-effacing, abandoning all that is "ours" to become as theocentric as grace permits. We should become recollected and empty ourselves so as to leave room for the divine operation of the Holy Ghost.

This does not mean that all interior acts of petition, repentance, hope and gratitude will, or even should, cease. What it does mean is that such acts will be infused with adoration. Petition will tend towards joyous submission to Divine Providence; repentance to acknowledgement of the gulf between our void and God's Being; hope to the fulfillment in the love of possession of our present love of desire of God through faith; gratitude, as in the *Gloria*, to giving God thanks "for His great glory." This is what adoration is: divine love returning to the Father through the medium of us creatures. It is the ultimate object of all prayer.

It must not be imagined that such a view of prayer may be descriptive of high contemplatives in the unitive way but cannot be applied to the simple faithful. Yes it can. All the forms of prayer peculiar to and encouraged by the Church imply and require a state of recollection and adherence, not of meaningful commitment and activity. The Rosary, the Litanies, the Stations, the Divine Praises, indulgenced ejaculations—in what possible way are such repetitions "meaningful?" Their use is to reduce the activity of the human mind to a minimum in order to liberate the soul for adherence to God in prayer. But far more important than in any devotion, this same state of recollection and adherence was required in the supreme act of worship: the Mass.

I learned to say my prayers at my mother's knee—and I still say the same ones each night. But I learned to pray when I was dragged off to Mass on Sundays. Something was altered with Mummy and Daddy. They did not talk to each other or even look at each other. Mummy usually fiddled with a Rosary. Daddy thumbed intermittently a *Garden of the Soul* which one of my nephews still uses. My eldest sister, Gertrude, who became a Benedictine nun, knelt bolt upright with her eyes usually shut. As I looked round it was the same with all our other relatives and neighbours. What was most unusual was that nobody paid the slightest attention to me. Even if I pulled Mummy's skirt, she just gently pushed me away. I once tried to climb on Daddy's back; he lifted me off and put me under the seat. That, too, was strange: although I was in my Sunday best, I was allowed to crawl about the floor provided I did not make a noise. Funny little boy that I was, I realized perfectly well that something was up.

Over there at the altar was Father Gray, a stern old man. I used to hide in the lavatory when he came to visit us. He was dressed in brightly coloured clothes and looked like a fat butterfly. Most of the time he said nothing. He was looking the other way and paid as little attention to Mummy and Daddy as they paid to me.

I do not think that I was a particularly precocious child but I was certainly very young when I tumbled to the fact that all these people were praying without saying prayers, as I did. Children are imitative: I too wanted to pray without saying prayers. I opened up to my sister Gertrude. "Just sit quite still, like a good boy," she said. "You are too small to kneel. Keep your hands still as well, on your thighs. Try not to look round and keep your eyes shut if you can. Then just say 'Jesus' under your breath, slowly but constantly. I'll prod you when you say 'Thou art my Lord and my God' and you can say it with me."

That, *mutatis mutandis*, is I suppose how we all learned to pray. The point I am getting at is that the Mass itself was our school of prayer. It was there that we learned to be self-effacing, detached, recollected and to adhere to the Divine Presence. It was also at Mass that the simple faithful practiced prayer throughout their lives. They may have known little theology but they prayed as theologians often do not. Moreover, the simplest of them attained to heights of prayer and sanctity far beyond me.

Therein lies the tragedy of the New Ordo. Although its theology is ambiguous and its liturgical theory abysmal, those are not what I hold principally against it. The real trouble is that the New Ordo is unprayable. For seven long years I have both celebrated and attended it. It presents itself as a human action, an event, requiring participation; instead of a divine action, The Event of the Sacrifice of God Incarnate, requiring adherence. On the one side you have self-effacement, recollection and adherence, on the other self-expression, self-commitment and participation; these are irreconcilable. And the New Ordo does not merely call for its specific attitudes, it enforces them. You cannot be recollected with a microphone blaring at you in your native tongue which you cannot help but understand. You cannot be self-effacing if you have got to stand up and answer up. You cannot adhere to God if you are busy shaking hands all round. I shall not go into details, illuminating though they be.

Yes, that is the tragic triumph of the "renewal"; it has destroyed the source, the school and the practice of prayer. . . .

◇　◇　◇

II

45. Four short extracts from Letters on the Subject of Prayer.

A. I am so glad you found my talk a help rather than a hindrance. What you say is absolutely true: "Adoration is not our love of God but God's love in us. Our prayer is real not because we say 'Lord, Lord', but because the Holy Ghost cries 'Abba, Father.' " That is why there must be a process of self-emptying: our acts, even of love, must give way to, make room for the divine act. We can only experience the Infinite when we have ceased to experience the finite.

This is true. But to empty ourselves is not to despise ourselves. On the contrary, we must exult in this strange creature which God has created with the capacity to reach up to its Creator. Even fallen nature is a wonderful thing since we can conceive God; redeemed nature is still more wonderful since we can possess Him—or, to speak more accurately, we can know that He possesses us. I doubt if there can be true devotion without a sense of awe and marvel at all creation, including ourselves. I mention this because you seem to be tempted in that direction. You should not have a low opinion of yourself for the simple reason that you should not have an opinion of yourself at all. . . .

B. Please do not ask me about "states of prayer." Just as you commit a sin of pride the moment you think how humble you are, so prayer ceases the moment you become self-conscious about it. That "states of prayer" exist objectively I have not the least doubt, but the person who prays can never know his own state. The moment he thinks he does he has gone down to the bottom of the

170

ladder and will probably stay there. We adore; but woe betide him who picks up a mirror to see himself at it! All he will see is his own void.

C. No, of course the theocentricity of prayer does not make it anti-social. On the contrary. All our pious self-exhortations and resolutions to love our neighbour might help us to be reasonably polite to him and exercise well-intentioned hyprocrisy, but they cannot make us love him because they remain mere human acts. But real prayer, in which we forget our neighbour as ourselves in order to adhere to God, will so perfect us that, to our own surprise, we shall suddenly distinguish in that neighbour something lovable and before unseen. This is the operation of grace.

D. I must have expressed myself badly. I regard meditation as highly important, particularly in the form of spiritual reading—in which it is not our own thoughts we think. There is no sanctity without ascetics, that is to say without disciplining the body and senses by mortification and disciplining the mind and imagination by meditation. But meditation is not prayer. It is directed towards self-perfection, whereas prayer is directed towards the adoration of God. Moreover, if not properly handled, meditation can become the most insidious of all distractions: we can become self-satisfied with the piety of our own thoughts. On the whole, meditation should be in depth, fathoming a very simple thought. One should avoid flitting from one pious thought to another. Take St Thais, for example. Upon her conversion this holy penitent went to Abbot Paphnutius for spiritual guidance. "Just sit facing East," said he, "and repeat nothing but the words 'Thou who hast made me have mercy on me—*Qui plasmasti me, miserere mei.*'" This she did for three years until she became a paragon of prayer. A trifle austere, perhaps, but the nature of the advice is sound.

◇   ◇   ◇

46.   A Longer Letter on Prayer.
Certainly mental and physical attitudes help or hinder prayer. We are trying to make love to God. The suitor who

171

does nothing but moan, cadge and talk about himself is unlikely to be successful. "O my God! O my gout!" is not the best mental attitude in which to pray. The mind must be alert and fixed on the Beloved. Incidentally, "recollection" is not synonymous with "depression." On the contrary, the more alert the mind the quicker it will become recollected. And this alertness and attention to the Beloved should find physical expression. Hence one should smile but keep one's eyes shut.

Clearly the best positions for the body are to kneel or sit. Walter Hilton, if I remember correctly, was a great believer in sitting. Standing is a different matter. Not only is it uncomfortable after a little while but it is difficult to know what to do with the hands—the most expressive members of our body. To hold the arms out cruciform is one solution. To hold them out in front of one with elbows slightly bent and palms upwards, shoulder-high, in the attitude of begging, is another. These positions, however, require space and are blush-making in public. You will notice, incidentally, that the priest in the old Mass stood most of the time. Yes, but the movements of his hands were very carefully regulated. This was completely right. Also, he had his back to the congregation so as to allow him liberty in his facial expression.

It is obviously a minor point, but this is one of the details which make the New Ordo unprayable. The faithful are supposed to stand in a circle or semicircle around the Table. They are obliged to cling, as though drowning, to the chair in front or their arms droop at their sides or are crossed belligerently on their chest. Neither they nor the priest have liberty of facial expression. Since they are all staring at each other, only one expression is possible: that of total boredom. It proves beyond doubt that the authors of the New Ordo were liturgists but not men of prayer.

Concerning prayers of petition, it is quite easy to see the spirit in which they should be made. How horrid are children who always say "giv'me"; how charming are those who ask, "May I leave the table?" You can analyse the difference yourself.

◇　◇　◇

III
FAILURE

47. A "Second" Talk.

(It has been very difficult to decipher as it was clearly written in great haste in a sort of shorthand.)

It is a very different matter to know something in the abstract and to experience its reality. I was well aware that your Congregation was among the most progressive in the country but I had no means of picturing what this really meant. Now I can see you in front of me, all forty-two ladies from your three establishments in this diocese.

The first thing to strike me is, obviously, your appearance. How I admire the ingenuity with which you manage to vary it. Of old, you were in habit, coif and veil. One saw nothing more than your eyes, nose, mouth and hands. How simple it was! Now it has become very complicated. I have not taken an exact count, but you have over twenty different hairstyles. Deep meditation must have gone into such a result. I admire each, although three of you spoil the effect by wearing mantillas here in the chapel. And what a variety of suits, jumpers, frocks! Not two alike. But what I admire most—being a man although a Bishop—is your forty-two varieties of shoes. I have not noticed one pair the same. This is astounding. It must be the result of much prayerful thought.

We are all well aware that the modern world is deeply concerned about pollution and the environment. You look wonderfully clean, so physical pollution is no problem. But has it never struck you that your clothes are your immediate environment? They both condition and express you. Of old your habit expressed your vows and your Congregation. They also conditioned your reaction to people and—more important—their reaction to you. Now they express no more than yourselves. How they condition your reaction to people, I can only guess. How they condition people's reaction to you is clear. You are females. The members of your own sex will show you little mercy. As for men, were I not a Bishop, I might easily pinch some of the more rotund bottoms. Is that what you want?

Hair-dos, shoe cleaning, clothes cleaning, washing and ironing—it must all take a considerable time. I am not in the least surprised that the half-hour meditation before Mass should no longer be compulsory. What does seem to me odd is that Mass itself has become optional. But so has everything else. As several of you put it to me during interviews: "We now do freely what we did under compulsion." This you consider to be a great improvement. I have two observations to make.

1. I grant it to be true that you now do freely what you did by force. The distinction is important. You are the dedicated Spouses of Christ to whom, consequently, you have obligations. You are not His mistresses, whom you are willing to oblige. You must have been told a hundred times that the supreme act of liberty lies in its surrender, be it in marriage, be it to God. That is what is meant by love: the will of the lover surrenders to the Beloved. Since when have you decided that your freedom is worth more than your vows and that your independence is a greater virtue than your obedience to the Rule?

2. But in fact it is quite untrue that you now do freely what you did by force. You have a *rota* for your Office. There are no longer community devotions. At meals, you come in when you like, you sit where you like, there is no reading and you talk as you please. This afternoon during interviews I was not impressed by the silence of your house. But what strikes me as most strange is your freedom in spiritual reading. I asked each of you what you read. Out of the forty-two only four were reading recognizably spiritual books. Most of you admitted to reading nothing spiritual at all. Five of you drew your spirituality from a couple of curious Karls—Marx and Rahner.

My dear ladies, you live in community but you no longer belong to one. You are a group of independent spinsters held together, presumably, by habit and self-interest.

How have the Old Men crept into the walled garden where chaste Susanna once bathed so gaily in the fountain of eternal life? They have unbolted the door from within. The crowd has surged forward and trampled the flowers underfoot. The garden is a sea of mud. And where is Susanna? She has vanished in the crowd. But how have the Old Men got there?

I suppose the mass media play their part. As the taxi turned into your drive, I could see the horns of your aerial standing proudly above your convent. In your parlour I noticed a fairly wide selection of newspapers. I wonder how much peace of mind you reap from the mass media? Are journalists so incompetent that they never succeed in influencing your outlook? The mass media carry you to the summit of that exceeding high mountain whence you can see all the kingdoms of the world and the glory and the shame thereof. What was a temptation to Jesus, is it none to you?

But the mass media alone would not account for the presence of the Old Men. They might make you less vigilant to guard the gate but would not let them in. However, both in your parlour and in your library I noticed a crowd of books and trendy reviews of theological fiction. How easy it is for the Old Men to slip in between the pages!

Fashionable theology, my dear ladies, is the worst conceivable guide to eternal life. Instead of stooping to scour that intellectual dustbin, why do you not stretch your souls to breaking point in the contemplation of God? You will learn more theology by adoring the Divine Reality than by absorbing men's imaginings. Besides, prayer is an exercise at which your sex excels because it is an activity of the will. Although I have met some singularly stupid women, rarely have I met one who lacks courage and will-power. God has made you that way.

Why do you not steep your minds in the spiritual writers of your own sex? The great St Teresa is no more to be feared than the Little Flower is to be despised. There are Saints Catherine of Genoa and Siena as well as Catherine Labouré; Gertrude and Mechthild of Helfta; Bridget of Sweden, Angela of Foligno, Colomba of Rieti, Juliana of Norwich, Jeanne de Chantal, Margaret Mary; and among lesser stars Lady Lucy Herbert and Cécile Bruyère—the list is endless. Myself, I have been more influenced by such women than by any man with the exception of St Francis de Sales, whose *Treatise on the Love of God* was written for a woman, Saint Chantal. Merely to see how these women prayed stretches the soul. We become capable in our little way of imitating the Mother of God: our soul too "magnifies the Lord" and our spirit too "exults in God our Saviour." The world shrivels and de-

175

presses, the spirit exalts and expands. A ltttle more spirituality may give you the energy to repair the garden wall, so that once more chaste Susanna can bathe gaily in the fountain of eternal life.

But I have no illusions, my dear ladies. What I say must seem to you as meaningless as the braying of Balaam's ass. Like Balaam, it would require an angel to stand here with a drawn sword for you "to fall to the ground in worship" (*Nbs* 22-31).

◇   ◇   ◇

48.   Two letters.

(Of the following two letters there are eleven of the first type and five of the second, involving eight nuns.)

A.   I strongly advise you to stay where you are. Your Congregation is by no means hopeless. I have seen far worse. Moreover, your Superior is a perfectly sensible woman and you have a very worthy chaplain. It should not be difficult to organize in your convent a group of Sisters who would obey the Rule in all things spiritual. This could even be done with the approval of your Superior—to whom, if you like, you can show this letter. Just imagine what would happen if all the nuns who loved their Rule and honoured their vows were the ones to leave their Convents! I also feel quite certain that the restoration of the Immemorial Mass in your chapel will gradually alter the whole atmosphere of your convent.

B.   Your admirably clear letter confirmed what I suspected when I interviewed you both. Your vows were taken to your Rule and not to your Provincial, Mother General or the Congregation for Religious. Not only is the Rule no longer obeyed in your congregation but it is both physically and spiritually impossible for any individual or group of Sisters to attempt to obey it in the existing atmosphere. Of this I am quite certain. I therefore advise you both to go to Horethorpe Court at the end of this term. Miss Ruth Crashaw, who is in charge of the Court, used to be the Provincial of the Veronican Sisters. She is

176

an admirable woman and will be able to advise you. She will certainly exert no pressure to make you join her association of lay ladies.

It is, of course, earnestly to be hoped that your Provincial will arrange for there to be at least one convent where your Rule can be obeyed. This may take time. In the meantime, remain at the Court.

I am sending a copy of this note both to your Superior and to Miss Crashaw.

◇　◇　◇

IV

49.　Example of two talks by Bishop Forester on subjects other than prayer.

A.　Notes for a First Talk
Considerations:

1.　God is the primary concern of religion, yet God is rarely the subject of a sermon or matter for meditation.

2.　This is not unnatural since we cannot understand, comprehend, grasp God.

3.　Indeed, it is precisely when humans imagine that they can understand, comprehend, grasp God, that He vanishes. Humans are left with a void in the imagination and an empty grasp.

4.　My imagination and understanding are bound to limit God, to reduce Him to my size; whereas God is precisely He who is Eternal, Infinite, Omnipotent and TRANSCENDS ALL THINGS, including my comprehension.

5.　The atheist is right to deny his idea of God; where he is wrong is to deny His being.

6.　God is transcendent. He is outside, other than, apart from all creation. The creation depends entirely on Him but He does not depend in any way on it. If nothing was, God would not be altered. The creation reveals Him because without Him it would not be. It hides Him because nothing in the creation is He. That is why religion is a game of hide-and-seek.

177

7. But humans itch for an idol, for a God they can imagine and grasp. Inevitably they will think of Him as evolving instead of Eternal, as indefinite instead of Infinite, as the driving force of the creation instead of Omnipotent, as IMMANENT instead of TRANSCENDENT.

8. Yes immanent: to them God is not outside, other than, apart from all creation, but is inside the creation as the spirit which animates it. He is not a hidden God, beyond our imagination and grasp, but is immediately recognizable in all things, be it in one's neighbour or in the discoveries of science. The more we know and love the world, the more we know and love God. It is impersonal pantheism.

9. Such is the idol. It is adored by many Catholics today.

10. There is a sense in which God can be said to be immanent. It is not because He is in all things but because all things are in Him: "in Him we live and move and have our being."

11. Provided we are faithful, we need not fear lest we adore the idol instead of God, living and true. Our whole religious attitude should imply our belief in the constant interference in His creation of a transcendent God outside it. The Incarnation, the objective sacrifice of the Mass, the Sacraments working *ex opere operato*, divine Providence, all these would be nonsense if we did not believe in a transcendent God.

12. The worshippers of the idol believe only in nature. But there is no such thing. The reality is either "fallen nature" or "redeemed nature," the infranatural and the supernatural.

13. Those who believe in the supernatural are inevitably accused of being superstitious by those who do not. Let it not worry you. Superstition may sometimes be silly but it implies a generous attitude, a willingness to believe. The danger lies in its opposite, INFRASTITION, to believe less than the evidence warrants. It is not only wrong but mean.

14. Besides, if superstition is sometimes connected with

178

belief in the supernatural, the infranatural is a direct result of infrastition. Just look around you at the state of morality today, at the standard of human acts. . . .

B. Notes for a Second Talk with a Meditation in front of the Blessed Sacrament
    Considerations:

1. God, who wants for nothing, nonetheless wants my love; He is a jealous God.

2. God, outside whom nothing is, is nonetheless a usurer. He plants my being and gives increase by His grace, but He still expects to reap my virtues.

3. He has no more need of my virtues than of my love, so why should He be jealous and a usurer? It cannot be for His own sake; it must then be for mine.

4. If God so loved the world that He gave His only begotten Son, it is not because the world is lovable but because His jealousy is totally disinterested.

5. God has nothing to gain by His Incarnation, Passion and Death. I have everything to gain.

6. But even here, in His very act of revelation, He is still hiding: hiding in the womb of the Virgin Mary, hiding in a stable manger, hiding in Egypt, in Nazareth; ever revealing, ever hiding, up to the crowning paradox of the Cross.

7. It is a divine game of hide-and-seek in which He hides in order to be found—just as my mother did when I was a little boy.

8. Yes, and we do find Him, although we can never catch Him. It is He who catches us the moment we find Him.

9. Could any one of us deny our faith? I have tried, God forgive me! It cannot be done. This is because it is not we who catch but we who are caught.

10. We know, too, God's final hiding place, the strangest, most unlikely place of all: the Adorable Sacrament of the Altar.

179

11. It is there that we get caught. Where we appear to receive God, it is there that He receives us.

Meditation on the Considerations.

1. Here, O my God! is Your most secret hiding-place.

2. In the creation You hide in life and being. Here You hide in death and destruction. This is the memorial of Your Passion.

3. What You left us by Your testament was Your Body and Blood, the physical evidence of the most impossible of all crimes: deicide, the killing of God.

4. And we, mankind, are the culprits.

5. We talk much in our days of communal activity and shared responsibility. Such talk contains this much truth: in front of You, truly present on the altar, we share in the community and responsibility of guilt.

6. There is the victim; here is the culprit. What further evidence is there required for our condemnation?

7. But it is here, where You are most hidden, that You most reveal Yourself: *"omnipotentiam tuam parcendo maxime et miserando manifestas" (X p. Pent.)*. It is in sparing and pitying that Your omnipotence is supremely evident. In comparison to this, the creation is an insignificant bauble.

8. In Your hands the evidence of the most inconceivable crime becomes the guarantee of the criminal's forgiveness.

9. Because You are almighty, to you "all things work to a good end"—even the greatest possible crime. This is the act of the transcendent God, living and true.

10. Such is the luminous cloud in which is hidden and revealed the God of Christians—and there is none other.

11. Let us adore in silence lest the spoken word create an idol and shatter the reality.

◇   ◇   ◇

V

50.   The Result.
A letter to Miss Ruth Crashaw, Superior of the Ladies of the Veil at Horethorpe Court.
Palm Sunday, April 3rd, 1977.

Dear ex-Mother Provincial,

I have now seen practically every nun in the diocese. The result is in the hands of Divine Providence. At the moment it seems to me negligible. Indeed, I have perhaps done more harm than good by turning an uneasy peace into open conflict. However, I could not die with the nuns on my conscience. Besides, I have met some wonderful women and have witnessed suffering nobly borne.

I think I have been helpful to a number of individual Sisters and confirmed two Superiors in their determination to preserve some semblance of their Rule. That is my consolation and I suppose it is better than nothing. But in my simplicity—or vanity—I thought it would be enough to talk about God and prayer for everything to fall into place and return to order. Well, it hasn't. As I gave my little talks, I could see the faces harden where I had expected them to soften; I could feel the atmosphere grow cold where I had expected it to warm with enthusiasm.

I do not blame the nuns. They are not the culprits but the victims of this terrible collapse. The process of brainwashing has been going on in the convents openly since 1963, and surreptitiously for a decade before that. Moreover, in practice nuns are obliged to conform to their community, irrespective of their Rule. Little did they realize that their Rule was their Charter of Liberties. Once it went, they had no alternative but to conform.

Much of the responsibility for the collapse of the convents rests on the shoulders of the Sacred Congregation for Religious. Just think of the endless inquiries, circulars, recommendations, notifications and commissions which it sent out or set up. The Superiors were smothered in bumf and the nuns choked in conferences. If you ever have time, you ought to make a catalogue of all the directives you received from your Mother General or direct from the Congregation while you were Provincial. It would be illuminating.

However, the principal responsibility lies fairly and squarely on my own shoulders. True, the rot started long before the Council and before I became bishop—in about 1955, with advanced courses for nuns leading to internal degrees. I happened to know six of the professors; two were from this diocese, of whom one was Sludge. They were intelligent enough but all desperately progressive. Looking back, that was doubtless the criterion on which they were chosen. Psychologically they were all curiously alike: chipped, embittered men. They were very conscious of their intellectual superiority and had doubtless pictured themselves as predestined for a brilliant ecclesiastical career. For some reason or other they were ecclesiastical failures and lacked the humility to accept it. I was well aware of this and could have interfered effectively after I became bishop. I did not. My motive was charity to them. But it was a charity for which the nuns, not I, had to pay—and how dearly! More harm is done by charity at the expense of others than by direct injustice. Even in civil life, a miscarriage of justice is less harmful to society than charity to hardened criminals.

Then there were the brilliant young priests who gave you your countless retreats and days of recollection. What a gang! I knew it but never vetoed them or suggested an alternative. It would not have hurt me to give a few myself. I have waited until now when it is too late.

And how slack I was in the appointment of chaplains. My concern was not with the consumer, the nuns, but to find somewhere to place difficult priests. I sent a drunk to . . . and a hypochondriac to . . . At Horethorpe I gave you Sludge. Again I was exercising charity at your expense.

The fact is that all of the people committed to my spiritual care those to whom I gave the least attention and consideration were those who deserved it most: the dedicated virgins, Spouses of Christ.

Enough breast-beating.

The eight nuns whom I have recommended to you are all devout and sensible women, no cranks among them. They would have left their respective congregations anyway and for legitimate reasons. I am pretty sure that they will not return. This does not mean, however, that I think they should join you permanently at the Court.

This is what is going through my mind. Of the eight, six

are teachers. Two of them, ____ and ____, are quite first class. Of the eleven ladies you have already collected, four are also teachers. This gives a nucleus of ten nun teachers. Now, it seems to me that you and the nine non-teachers should form one group or congregation and the teachers another, each with its own constitution and Superior. You would be basically contemplatives; your work would be to look after the seminary and give retreats to nuns. The teachers would teach. The convent at Peddicombe will be closing anyway in July from lack of nuns rather than of pupils. The Trust could buy it and rent it to the teachers. They would turn it into a first class girls' boarding school in which the Faith would be preserved.

We can discuss the matter when next we meet. That is not the only subject on which I shall need the guidance of your wisdom and experience.

CHAPTER VIII

FAITH AND PRACTICE

51.   Third letter to Henry Dobson, Bishop of Hunstanton.
(The first is #6 and the second #36.)
Friday, March 11th, 1977.

Dear Harry,

It was most kind of you to come and see me. I thoroughly enjoyed your visit. You are always so stimulating. Besides, you save me the trouble of wading through the latest nonsense: you expound it so succinctly and clearly yourself.

I am of course sorry that you will not promise to ordain my men in case of necessity. I suppose that I should not have hoped for more than your favourable prejudice. We humans have an itch to distrust God's Providence. He will see to their ordination as He has to their vocation.

You know, during the course of conversation I think we touched on one of the basic problems in the Church today. I was holding forth on the fact that the Church is guardian of the Faith and the present crisis arose because what she enjoins and permits in practice is not readily recognizable as an expression of the Faith she guarantees. Hence we could arrive at the absurd situation in which practicers had lost the Faith whereas the faithful refused to practice. It was your answer to this which seems to me so important. You said: "There is only one object of Faith: the Church. I am baptized into the Church and it is she who gives me Faith. On her authority I believe all other doctrines. She can deal with them as she likes, since she is the only constant. Christ revealed no doctrines but a praxis: His Kingdom the Church." We left it at that.

Few people, I think, could formulate the argument as honestly and clearly as you. Nevertheless, I believe it expresses the basic attitude of countless Catholics today, not of the "modernists" but of those who simply obey. It is a very ecclesiastical argument, akin to the patriotism in "My country right or wrong." But is it true?

I suspect that it rests on two articles in the old catechism:

1. Faith is a supernatural gift of God enabling me to believe without doubting whatever God has revealed.

2. I am to know what God has revealed by the teaching, testimony and authority of the Catholic Church.

If one puts those two articles together, one gets the impression that Faith as a supernatural gift merely empowers a person to believe what the Church teaches and the objects of Faith are provided by the Church. It is therefore the Church which justifies the Faith and not the Faith which justifies the Church. Hence the Church must be obeyed in all things, even if she is quite clearly hiding her light under a bushel. It automatically becomes right and proper that the light should be so shaded because legitimate authority in the Church has said so. I do not think that is an unfair or distorted presentation of the case, is it?

But surely it is evident that such an argument is tautological or a vicious circle? I am to know what God has revealed by the authority of the Church. And how am I to know that the Church has such authority? Because the Church says that God has revealed it. It is patently nonsense.

You will notice that you yourself admit it to be nonsense. You said: "Christ revealed no doctrines but a praxis: His Kingdom, His Church." You thereby concede that there is at any rate one object of Faith logically prior to the Church: the authority of Christ. And once you admit that, all the rest follows. Is His authority divine? Is He God incarnate, the Second Person of the Trinity, born of the Virgin Mary, etc.?

Indeed, one of the things which follows from your prior faith in the divine authority of Christ is the authority of the Church. It does not work the other way round: you do not believe that Christ receives His authority from the Church. The Church is the guardian of God's revelation but not its source. She herself is one of the objects of Faith: I believe in One, Holy, Catholic and Apostolic Church.

Therein, it seems to me, lies the crux of the present crisis. I mean the crisis between honest Catholics, such as I believe both of us to be. I am not referring to heretics who have lost the Faith although the Church no longer excludes them. I mean you and me. Faced with the same crisis, we react in diametrically opposite ways. Your immediate reaction, along with the overwhelming majority of churchmen, is to save the Church and the Faith will look after itself. Mine, along with a heavy percentage of the laity, is to save the Faith and let the Church look after herself. We cannot both be right. Indeed, each day the gulf between us is growing wider. If we pursue our ways indefinitely we shall come to the point when the faithful are legal schismatics and the obedient factual heretics.

At this point I can hear you say: "Don't talk rot, Edmund. It is your metaphor which deceives you. We are not going in opposite directions: we are merely looking at the opposite facets of the same coin. Even if I grant you the logical priority of Faith over the Church, in practice he who defends the Church defends the Faith and he who defends the Faith defends the Church."

In normal times this would by and large be so. I say "by and large" because history provides plenty of examples of excessive use of ecclesiastical authority. Quite apart from mediaeval excommunications, in our own day some of your friends might feel that Pius XII went a bit far when he demanded internal assent to the Five Ways of proving the existence of God. But at this moment of time it is patently untrue to say that in defending the Church one is automatically defending the Faith and this for two reasons: a) the Faith is ambiguously formulated; b) heretics are no longer excluded from the Church. The fact is that the Faith is exclusive whereas the Church has become inclusive. She has changed Our Lord's lapidary sentence, "He who is not with me is

187

against me," into the coward's whine, "He is my friend who bullies me."

We do not have to look very far for the result, my dear Harry. Concerning the defence of the Faith, over the past ten years have you promoted priests who refuse the term and doubtless the meaning of "Transubstantiation" and talk of "a Personal" instead of "The Real Presence?" I have. What have you done about clergy who openly preach contraception? A little more, I hope, than I—which is practically nothing. Has your natural chivalry, if not your conviction, led you to defend the Mother of God against those who "put her in her place?" It has not me. Have you remonstrated with those who refuse to administer the Sacrament of Penance except by appointment but insist on Penitential Services? As a matter of fact I have, but I trust you have done it more firmly. Have you stamped on priests who refuse to give infant Baptism for a variety of specious reasons including the denial of Original Sin? I have done little more than wag a reproving finger accompanied by a rueful smile. Have you even defended the authority of the Papacy and your own against the democratic rights of the People of God? Curiously enough, you probably less than I, which is not saying much. I call a halt to this catalogue not from lack of ammunition but of patience. The fact is, and we know it, that in our own dioceses it is not we who have defended the Faith; it has been left to pathetic little groups of layfolk, helped or hindered by a stray priest, to do so.

It is a very different matter when it comes to enforcing the New Outlook. Have you promoted a priest who has stuck to the Immemorial Mass? Of course not and, to my everlasting shame, neither have I. What has been your attitude to priests who mumble that Vatican II failed to face the facts and that post-Conciliar legislation has been disastrous; who refuse to be brainwashed by attending compulsory study-days; who jeer at Bishops' Collegiality, the National Conference of Priests and the new structures generally; who will not give Communion standing and in the hand; who administer Extreme Unction as of yore; who still say the Breviary, the Rosary and make their meditation; who . . . ? Have you reserved key positions in your administration for such men of probity and principle? No more than I have, Harry. We have looked after the Church all right but not after the Faith.

The crowning example is Archbishop Lefebvre. He has

been attacked from all sides, yet nobody has dared impugn his Faith and accuse him of being unorthodox. In fact, if only he would utter the tiniest, wee little heresy, authority could indulge in charity and all would be forgiven. The trouble is that the old devil won't, so there is nothing to forgive. Thus he gets suspended and threatened with excommunication on a trumped up charge of disobeying ecclesiastical law.

My own case is not without its interest. I do nothing which I have not got a perfect right to do. I endeavour to mend the divisions in my diocese precisely by appealing to the unity of Faith against the "divisiveness" of praxis. This so horrifies authority that it first reveals the fact that I am dying and then will not let me die in peace. I have here on my desk a letter from Klushko summoning me to Rome. Perhaps he hopes that the voyage will kill me! Of course I shall not go. If he is all that keen on a chat, he can come to Stamford.

Somewhere towards the start of this epistle I said that we might end up in the absurd position where practicing Catholics had lost the Faith whereas the faithful refused to practice. We are there already. Although, as a bishop, I am rather cut off from intimacy with the laity, among my personal friends I know a surprising number of people in that position. I shall give you an example. It is one among many but it happened to hurt me quite particularly.

When I was a little boy the only other Catholics in our vicinity were the Fogartys, a very devout and respectable family from Galway. Mr Fogarty was cowman on a neighbouring estate. One of the children, Kate, was my age. I have known her all my life and love her dearly. She married an excellent Catholic fellow from Epping. Whenever I had to drive up to London, I tried to arrange to have lunch with Kate and her husband on the way. The last time I did so was in October. I was a bit early and Robert, the husband, had not returned from work. "Oh, Edmund! I am so glad to get you alone," said Kate. "It's about Robert. Can't you say something to him? He refuses to go to Mass, he who was so regular. He slangs the priests for everything. It's such a bad example for the grandchildren, etc." Robert duly turned up. Kate retired to the kitchen to serve up lunch. "Glad to get you alone," said Robert. "It's about the wife. Can't you put some sense into her? Madge, that's my eldest granddaughter, is going out with a non-Catholic. She says he needn't become a Catholic and they can get married in the Protestant church. She's put her on the pill, too, getting my Madge into wicked ways. And she's gone all politics. Communist, that's what I calls it. She spends her time at meetings and comes home full of hate. There's no more family Rosary. I say it by myself while they watch the telly. She's a right pagan, she is. And she takes Our Blessed Lord in her hand as though He were a bit of chewing gum. I can't watch her: it makes me sick. She says she's not a Roman Catholic: 'I'm an Adult Christian,' is what she says. And it's all the fault of those bloody priests. They're not Catholics, they're devils, breaking up happy homes, that's what they are." Etc. . . . At lunch all I was able to do was to verify that both had spoken the truth. Kate practiced but had lost the Faith. Robert was faithful, even devout, but nothing would induce him to practice. How sad! And this is quite common, as you know full well.

Well, I suppose I shall have to answer Klushko. Before I do so, however, I should like to make my position clear.

The visible Church, the Kingdom, the community of the People of God—whatever you like to call it—is not the source but one of the objects of Faith; neither is she the sole nor even the primary object thereof. What she is, on the other hand, is the guardian of the Faith by divine authority. As such she is infallible in proclaiming what the Faith is. Being composed of mortal men, however, she is lamentably fallible in putting the Faith into practice. This capacity for practical error is just as present in the Church's administration as in her individual members. The Church is infallible but not impeccable. Where there is conflict between her Faith and her practice, as is clearly the case today, the faithful have no alternative but to cling to her Faith and discard her practice. My position is surely as reasonable as it is clear: I judge the Church's fallible practice in the light of her infallible Faith. In theory, my dear Harry, you are either maintaining that the Church is impeccable—which is nonsense—or that one should cling to her practice and abandon her Faith.

Fortunately, however, we none of us live by theories and I know that Harry Dobson is just as good a Catholic as he knows is

His devoted friend,
Edmund Forester.

◇   ◇   ◇

190

52.   Second letter to Archbishop Klushko, Rome.
     (The first letter is #35.)
Friday, March 11th, 1977.

Dear Archbishop Klushko,

First of all I must congratulate you on your new appointment. Not only does it immediately put you into a key position but, in view of your comparative youth, it means that with a modicum of care you can scarcely avoid becoming a Cardinal. This, I imagine, could still be quite fun—although the renewal of the Church in implementing the spirit of Vatican II has abolished the principal attraction of that high office. I refer, of course, to the hat.

I am in receipt of your letter of February 28th and apologize for the delay in answering it. It is most kind of you to invite me to Rome and under normal circumstances I should be delighted to accept. As you know, however, I happen to be dying. It is an inconvenient occupation which makes it difficult for me to move from my base: numerous injections, an impossible diet and inconsiderate bowels.

However, I should not like you to imagine that I am using my imminent demise as an excuse. Were I in the pink of health I should require some assurances and clarifications before accepting your invitation. You write: "The Cardinal Prefect and myself should now like to discuss with you odd points which cause us some embarrassment as a result of your *Ad clerum* of January 13th." Apart from the reference to my *Ad clerum*, this is word for word the same as Cardinal Garrone's letter to Archbishop Lefebvre of January 25th, 1975: "nous voudrions nous entretenir avec vous . . ." Diplomatic language, I suppose, follows well worn grooves. The point is, however, that when Lefebvre, all on his own without Canon Lawyer, theologian or secretary, arrived in Rome, he found himself confronted by Cardinals Garrone, Wright and Tabera sitting as a sort of People's Court in which the accusation is the condemnation. The Court proceedings were duly taped.

Now, I am willing to chat with anyone—presumably Testastorta as I am unable to get to Rome. I am also willing to appear (inevitably by proxy) in front of any tribunal provided that the case against me is properly formulated and I am given due notice; that I am allowed Counsel as I think fit; that I may myself have the proceedings recorded and publish them at my discretion. What I am unwilling to do is to turn up for a chat and come in for a grilling.

I wish to explain why I insist on recording and publishing myself any discussion or proceedings which may take place. You will remember that in the case of Archbishop Lefebvre the discussion of January 25th was duly taped. This was probably less to hear what Lefebvre had to say for himself than to make sure that the Cardinals did the grilling properly. Apparently they did not, so the tough old bird was put under the grill again on March 3rd. This time the Cardinals doubtless said all they were supposed to. Lefebvre asked for a copy of the tape. Garrone had no hesitation: of course, it was his right. That evening Lefebvre sent a person round to the secretary with the necessary machinery to re-record the tape. It was refused. Next day he went himself to get it. No, he could only have a transcript, which would be ready the following evening. The following evening he was told that even the transcript was not forthcoming. It is reasonably obvious that neither Garrone nor the secretary had the tape. It must have been removed by higher authority who refused to part with it. So Lefebvre never got a copy. Then came the crowning insult. Months later—quite recently in fact—extracts appeared in an illustrated French weekly! I lack the humility to lay myself open to such treatment.

Do not tapes remind you of something, my dear Archbishop? I am not wildly interested in politics, but I seem to remember a scandal in the United States about a watergate [sic]. The upshot of it was that the then President was obliged to produce the tapes which condemned him. Surely this was splendid? It proved to the world that the U.S. is a great and civilized country, governed in the long run by the Rule of Law no matter how much mud may collect in her watergates. I wish the Vatican had done likewise in the Lefebvre affair. As all agree, justice must not only be done but be seen to be done. Now that you are a distinguished member of the Church's central administration, I trust that you will exert your utmost influence to secure the re-establishment of the Rule of Law. The sanctuary of the post-Conciliar Church is sufficiently cluttered with corpses without adding it to the pile.

I am no less sincerely yours,
my dear Archbishop,
for remaining in indignant opposition,

53.   To the Reverend Bryan Houghton,
Avignon, France.
Sunday, March 13th, 1977.

Dear Bryan,
I do not know if you read the copies of my correspondence or if you merely file them. If you read them, you will notice that yesterday I wrote to Klushko mentioning the Lefebvre affair. It really is a scandalous business. I have never met Lefebvre nor corresponded with him but I took copious notes of whatever was published. Upon re-reading these notes I am so shocked that I intend to inflict the story on you. I hope it does not bore you stiff.

By no means does the scandal stop with the disappearance of the tapes. The Tribunal, you will remember, was composed of Cardinals Garrone, Wright and Tabera. I know nothing about Tabera but I met Garrone when he was Archbishop of Toulouse and from reliable sources have heard nothing but praise of Wright. These last two are quite certainly honourable men and it is out of keeping with their known character that they should deliberately have acted deceitfully. Thus when on January 25th Garrone invited Lefebvre to a chat, this is what he intended. Higher authority must have intervened to turn it into the grilling of February 13th and March 3rd.

Anyway, the Tribunal's verdict is dated May 6th, 1975. It is not devoid of interest.

In the first place, the sentence was executed before judgment was given. I wonder if this is unique in the history of law. Moreover, it was executed on the authority of Tabera, a member of the Tribunal. Yes, on April 25th, eleven days before the verdict was signed, Tabera wrote to Bishop Mamie of Fribourg "calling upon you to proceed without delay" to the suppression of Lefebvre's Confraternity of St Pius X. He gives for his authority "the conclusions reached by the special Commission of Cardinals"—but they had reached no conclusions at that date. The only explanation I can think of is that he was forcing his colleagues' hands, presumably on instructions from higher authority. Bishop Mamie obeyed. On May 6th, consequently on the very day that the verdict was signed and before he could conceivably have received a certified copy of it, he notified Archbishop Lefebvre that he and all his works ceased to exist: "This decision takes immediate effect."

The verdict of May 6th is a surprising document. The three clauses of condemnation are preceded by a covering letter. This reads like an exercise in dry humour. Here is what it says about the grilling: "We remain most grateful for the friendly atmosphere in which our recent discussions took place, without our differing points of view ever impairing the serene and deep fellowship between us (*communion profonde et sereine.*)" What a joke! The central argument is even more rum: "It is inadmissible that people should be called upon to pass their own personal judgement on orders emanating from the Pope, whether to submit or not: herein lies the traditional argument of the sects who appeal to yesterday's Pope to avoid obeying today's." Surely the Cardinals have their tongues in their cheeks? Inevitably all heretics appeal to tomorrow's Pope or the future Council, if not more radically to the Holy Ghost or the Second Coming—as do our Pentecostalists, Charismatics and Teilhardists today.

At last we come to the three clauses of the actual verdict. In each clause the operative words are in inverted commas. I need not expatiate on the significance of this astonishing fact. I quote them in full with the inverted commas:

1. "A letter shall be sent to Mgr Mamie by which is recognized his right to withdraw his predecessor's approbation of the Confraternity and its Statutes." The deed has been done by letter from His Eminence Cardinal Tabera, Prefect of the S. Congregation for Religious.

2. Once the Confraternity is suppressed, "no longer having any juridical basis, its offshoots, and notably the seminary at Ecône, cease by the same token to have the right to exist."

3. It is evident—and we are called upon to give clear notice thereof—"that no support may be given to Mgr Lefebvre so long as the ideas contained in his Manifesto of November 21st, 1974 shall remain the rule governing his actions."

Quite apart from the inverted commas, I love the insertion in clause 3: "and we are called upon to give clear notice thereof—*nous sommes invités à le notifier clairement*"! Has there ever been another judgment thus to proclaim itself a sham? I know that Cardinals Garrone and Wright have been criticized for signing the verdict. I disagree: honour must be given where it is due. They only signed to what had already been accomplished by Tabera and Mamie—and they say so. They also made it quite clear that the verdict was not theirs.

In view of the Cardinals' verdict and the suppression of his Confraternity by the Bishop of Fribourg, on May 21st Lefebvre appealed to the Supreme Court of the Church, the Segnatura. Its Prefect is one Cardinal Staffa, reputedly a man of principle. Lefebvre's grounds were threefold: 1. lack of legal form in the suppression of his Confraternity since, under Cn 493, only the Holy See, not the Bishop of Fribourg, could do so; 2. since he, Lefebvre, is condemned in matters of faith, the Congregation for the Doctrine of the Faith is alone competent and not Garrone's Tribunal; 3. a condemnation of his Declaration of November 1974 affects none but himself; it affects neither his Confraternity nor his Seminary. These grounds seem perfectly reasonable.

Ah, the dear old Segnatura! If Rome is hailed as the Eternal City, the Segnatura exemplifies what is meant. No panic, no flap at the Segnatura, all is seemliness and due decorum. When Lefebvre posted his appeal that evening of May 21st, he must have felt that perfect peace was his for at least a twelve-month.

Not a bit of it! His appeal was duly registered at the Segnatura on June 5th; its rejection is dated June 10th. What, overtime at the Segnatura? Impossible! Lefebvre's lawyer on the spot had a different explanation: Cardinal Villot sent a note in his own handwriting to Cardinal Staffa "directing him to prohibit the appeal."

On the face of it, this does not look too good: the highest administrative officer in the Church giving directions to the highest judicial officer. This would be worse than Watergate. But, admitting the physical fact of Villot's intervention, is this exactly what happened? In view of Staffa's reputation, I suspect not. It is worth looking at the wording of Staffa's rejection of the appeal. In the name of the Supreme Tribunal he declares himself "incompetent" under Canon 1556. And what says Cn 1556? *"Prima Sedes a nemine judicatur*—the Primatial See is judged by no one." This implies rather a lot:

195

that Tabera was right and prior to April 25th the Supreme Pontiff had by personal act condemned Lefebvre and all his works—presumably on the evidence of the vanished tapes; that the inverted commas in the Garrone verdict were quotations from this Papal condemnation and his tribunal was mere window-dressing; that Villot's note to Staffa was to inform the latter of the Supreme Pontiff's sentence; that Staffa did no more than record a fact. The trouble with all this is that the essential document is missing: the Papal decree condemning Lefebvre and all his works. One really cannot base public acts on private documents. The whole business is made to look shifty by the constant shifting between a judicial process and the appeal to a secret decree. Small wonder that Lefebvre should pay scant attention to his condemnation. Small wonder that I should lay down conditions to any interview with Klushko or his representative.

This is not quite the end of Act I in the Lefebvre tragedy. There are the two letters addressed to him by the Pope dated July 10th and September 10th, 1975. It is the first which needs to be examined, as the second is little more than a request for an answer. The Pope starts off by assuring Lefebvre that he is well informed of everything concerning his case and the seminary at Ecône. The tapes are not mentioned but I cannot help feeling that he is referring to them. He also shoulders full responsibility for ordering the immediate closure of Ecône—which ties in with Tabera's letter to Bishop Mamie of April 25th. Then comes the operative sentence demanding of Lefebvre "a public act of submission to the Council, to the post-Conciliar reforms and to the 'orientations' to which the Pope himself is pledged (*aux orientations qui engagent le Pape lui-même.*)" These three totally different things are all lumped together and Lefebvre is supposed to swallow the lot. Submission to the Council presents no difficulty. The documents it produced are wordy and ambiguous but are probably all right as far as they go. A legitimate criticism is that they do not go far enough—but that is a different matter. Submission to the "post-Conciliar reforms" needs a lot of clarification. Everyone, including Lefebvre, is doubtless willing to submit to those reforms which have been duly promulgated as soon as we know which they are: the New Ordo, for instance, is certainly not among them. Is Lefebvre supposed to submit to the administrative follies which are still

196

to come, apart from those which already exist? But to submit to the "orientations" to which the Pope feels pledged is perfectly preposterous. What a wonderfully vague word is "orientations": one's bearings, outlook, point of view, direction, party line. Up to and including the Council, Catholics were bound to believe in all defined doctrines and to obey the commands of the Church's magisterium. Now, apparently, we are expected to submit to an "outlook." We must all look in the same direction as the reigning Pontiff: "Company, eyes left!" This is giving us blinkers as never before. The new triumphalism is more exigent than the old. The trouble is that in a sense Paul VI is absolutely right: the new look in the Catholic Church is due precisely to the substitution of a human outlook for Divine Revelation. It is consequently largely sociological and political instead of dogmatic and spiritual. Heaven help us!

The end of the letter is no less curious. "You make yourself out to be a second Athanasius; but he was supporting the decrees of the Council of Nicaea whereas you are opposing Vatican II, which has no less authority than Nicaea and in many respects is more important." Exactly: Nicaea merely defined the Divinity of Christ, whereas Vatican II has given rise to an "orientation," an outlook. As a matter of fact, of course, Lefebvre is defending the decrees of all Councils, from Nicea to Vatican II inclusive: he is defending decrees as against "orientations."

Thus ends Act I. The plot is set. God alone can unravel it.

I hope I have not bored you with all this, but it has helped me a lot to put it down on paper. It was Klushko's letter which reminded me of Lefebvre. I made some notes on the affair in December 1975. On looking through them now, it seems more important and far sadder than it did at the time.

Now for less lugubrious subjects.

Apart from the Royal Family, your old friend and the Dowager of Blackwater probably possess the two best known faces in the country. Glauben rang me up last week to say that the fund had topped the million although the campaign for a "Duchess in every pub" was still in its infancy. Apart from the money, the enormous publicity will make it very difficult for my successor to undo what the Trust does. Glauben explained to me that this was his real object. Horethorpe has been paid for and the Trust has bought the Reparationist Fathers' house at Offleigh for a Teachers' Centre. Outman is over the moon. But you will receive a report about this before the next meeting of the Trust on April 14th. Incidentally, if you possibly can I think you ought to turn up. Your expenses will be paid and I can put you up. I know you are saying Mass at Tarascon on Easter Sunday but you could catch a plane at Marseilles on Tuesday. We should thus have a day together before the meeting.

The Association of St John Fisher is safe. By March 1st thirty-two priests had joined and there are now over fifty. It has become clear that, in the event of trouble, the Trust will be able to prevent the members from starving—not an unimportant consideration.

I have started my tour of the Convents. That is why I have not written to you. It completely exhausts me. In the little time I have I give them all I have; but it is not adequate. I doubt if I am getting anywhere, especially with the active orders. The rot is too far gone. So many of the convents possess a vicious little vixen of whom the old ducks are terrified: she rules the roost. I ought to have done the tour years ago. We bishops have been singularly remiss in looking after our nuns. Incidentally, the Mother Provincial of the Veronican Sisters has been expelled and laicized. She has turned up at the Court where she has a community of eleven. What a remarkable woman! I have great hopes that her influence will eventually spread to other convents. Her position is absolutely ridiculous and typical of the times: she and her companions obey the Rule and wear the habit but are technically laywomen; those who are technically Veronican Sisters are dressed as laywomen and do not obey the Rule.

I may not have time to write to you again before I see you. I so much look forward to your visit.

P.S. Socks called round the other day. The excuse was for a dispensation which he could have got from the V.G. He was as affable as usual but I am unable to respond. He made one curious remark: "Your advertising campaign is brilliant. I had never thought of it. It has changed the whole situation. You are appealing to the non-Catholics to force us to remain Catholic." It is very much what Glauben was saying.

◇ ◇ ◇

54.   To the Reverend Terence Daly, Deepdale.
(See letter 34.)
Tuesday, March 15th, 1977.

Dear Father Daly,

I was delighted to receive your letter and to learn that you have decided to try your vocation at Deepdale. I am convinced that the revival of the Church will come through the great Religious Orders once the present disorder has been washed away. I admit that over the past dozen years the Regulars have shown up worse than the Seculars but "corruption of best is ever the worst corruption." Anyway, I think Deepdale has the right mixture of agriculture and contemplation: down to earth and up to heaven, with no time for the world. Its religion is truly vertical and not horizontal.

You ask me what I think will be the future of the Church. My dear Father, I have not a clue. I am not a defeatist because I believe in God. On the other hand I am a great believer in failure because it gives Divine Providence a chance. It is because in this year of grace the Church has the appearance and odour of a dung-heap that God will use it to manure the most exquisite flowers, fragrant with the odour of sanctity. One simply does not know the future; but one knows He knows.

In spite of the warning in Holy Writ that God is a jealous God, we act as though He did not mind our constant interference. But He does mind. That is why the most carefully planned human activities normally turn out exactly contrary to plan. I cannot think of anything in my life which has turned out according to plan. I do not say that everything has turned out worse, far from it, but quite differently. For instance, I have just succumbed to the temptation to plan: I have arranged with two bishops to ordain the students at Horethorpe after my death. I do not know who will but I am quite sure that it will be neither of them.

This is not only true in private but also in public life. Plan democracy and you will get a tyranny; plan equality and fraternity to reap the Terror or a Gulag; plan Social Security and you will be lucky not to be murdered, mugged, thugged or kidnapped; plan wealth and you will go bankrupt. It is not that democracy, fraternity and the rest are bad things but they cannot be planned. When you try to, you will get the opposite. If humans stopped planning and attempted to obey the Commandments, then Divine Providence might lavish these benefits upon us.

Being a jealous God, He is quite particularly jealous of His Spouse, the Church. To plan His Church for Him is something which He resents. This is what we have been busy doing. We see the results. A "Pastoral" Council promptly scatters the flock; ecumenicity breeds a host of schisms; the most democratic of Popes becomes the most autocratic; the moment we bishops upgrade ourselves with "collegiality" we lose all authority; a Church suitable to the modern mind is enough to repel the bravest convert; give the faithful a comprehensible liturgy and they no longer know what it is about. Is it not wonderful? Surely, by the law of averages, some of the myriad plans ought to have worked. At least the Vatican tiddly-winks team should have beaten San Marino, or something, eh? Not a bit of it. Everything has gone contrary to plan. There under our eyes is an astonishing miracle, only explicable by direct intervention of Divine Providence.

Holding such views, I find it singularly difficult to prophesy. All I can say is that so long as the Church, from Pope to Parish Council, continues to plan we are in for a rough time. If, instead of planning, all these good people devoted a modicum of their energy to practicing the virtues, everything would fall into place. That is why I think you will do infinitely more good by digging and praying at Deepdale than you ever did in directing diocesan education. The difference will be that nobody will be able to see the good you do because it will work through Divine Providence, whereas everybody could see the mess you made of the schools because it worked through human planning.

Such are my real beliefs. However, I admit that prophecy is an amusing game of the imagination so long as one does not take it seriously and impinge on the reserve of the jealous God. Also, tea leaves probably provide more accurate data than statistics and trends. With this in mind I shall indulge in a little prophecy for our mutual amusement.

It seems to me that the principal victim of the renewal is the Papacy itself. In the century between the accession of Pius IX in 1846 and the death of Pius XII in 1958 it had acquired an authority and prestige which it had not enjoyed since the Middle Ages. It is thanks to this tradition of authority that the present Pope has been able to reform the Church from top to bottom as he likes in one short reign. The only trouble is that, in discarding every tradition in the Church, he has also discarded the tradition of Papal authority. Paul VI had the good fortune to ascend the throne of Pius XII but his successor will have the misfortune to ascend the throne of Paul VI. He will find chaos and lack authority and prestige to set it right. In actual fact, it may not be easy to elect a Pope at all. There may be a fairly long interregnum. I should not be in the least surprised (except that I shall be dead) if the interregnum ended with the election of two Popes—a Papal schism. After all, we have not had one since 1450 and another is overdue. Besides, it would fit in so neatly with the renewal. The avowed object of the renewal is the Reunion of the Churches, so God can scarcely avoid splitting the Church down the middle. The means by which the renewal has been imposed is by blind obedience to authority. A jealous God can dispose of that by making human authority uncertain. An attractive prophecy, my dear Father, don't you think so?

The imagination boggles at the prospect. Thanks to the mass media it would, of course, be practically impossible for anyone to know which was Pope and which anti-Pope. The anti-Pope could be installed in the Vatican with all the apparatus of government while the real one fled to a boarding-house in Malta. Naturally most governments would recognize the anti-Pope because they have such lovely embassies in Rome. The National Hierarchies, after the usual bout of prayerful thought, would exercise the virtue of prudence and fall in with their respective governments. The laity, irrationally but instinctively, would plump for the real Pope. The clergy would dither but in the long run follow their flock.

In the meantime the National Hierarchies will land in their own particular mess. In England, where revenue is already inadequate to maintain capital assets, the hierarchy will have to sell its churches and schools. For a brief moment the progressives will exult in their triumph: no ghetto schools and nothing but House Masses. But this revival of penal times will make the surviving clergy turn sharply back to tradition. In France it will be the other way round. The Cathedrals and churches will be intact because they belong to the State and the bishops cannot sell them, but there will be no clergy. Last

201

year fewer secular priests were ordained than there are bishops. Again, the progressives will get exactly what they want: community gatherings without a priest. The only people to attend, however, will be a few old diehards intent on saying the Rosary.—And so on among the members of the Federation of National Churches which has succeeded the One, Holy, Catholic and Apostolic Church.

Enough prophecy! I shall be serious again.

Whatever God holds in store for us in reward for our follies, I feel a reasonable confidence in three propositions.

1. The religion of Paul VI will not survive him—and this even if he lives long enough to promulgate his new Code of Canon Law expressly designed to perpetuate it. It is far too personal. It has no roots.

2. The traditionalists will survive in spite of being leaderless and divided. They have roots. Their vitality has already been proven by their surviving the utterly ruthless and brilliantly organized persecution by the official Church. They stand to gain either way: if there is a change of outlook at the death of Paul VI, or if the official Church enters a period of confusion.

3. The Great Orders will survive. Again, they have roots. Moreover, unlike the traditionalists, they are in the enviable position of being part of the official Church while having their own structures. Confusion in officialdom need scarcely affect them. They are a series of closed communities and all they need do is to stick to their Rule. It is true that most of them have bowed to the present storm but they would have little difficulty in holding high their heads once more. They would be unlikely to bend again. Indeed, this is what has happened at Deepdale. It is why I am so glad that you are joining that admirable community.

Remember me as you dig your potatoes and chant your Office. In the religious life these are the same thing.

◊   ◊   ◊

202

55.   To Bishop Tarquinio Testastorta, Apostolic Delegate
to Great Britain.
Friday, March 18th, 1977.

Dear Bishop Testastorta,

How remiss of me not to have congratulated you before on becoming a Bishop and Apostolic Delegate. I feel sure that your tact as Delegate will only be surpassed by your piety as bishop.

Thank you for giving me so clear an account of your telephone conversation with Archbishop Klushko. I am glad to know that his request for me to appear in Rome was purely a matter of form and that he understands my physical inability to comply.

Yes, I have heard of the American Jesuit, Harry Gaucher. I have even read one of his books, *The Existential Whitherness of Human Transcendence*, but it was a bit beyond me. I did not know that he was a personal friend of the Holy Father.

The time you suggest, 3 p.m. on Wednesday, April 13th, is not frightfully convenient for me as my friend Bryan Houghton will be turning up from France. However, I suppose you cannot alter it as it is the only day Fr Gaucher will be in England on his way to Rome from the States.

I clearly understand that it is only "an exploratory conversation." Nevertheless, as I wrote to Archbishop Klushko, I shall have it recorded in duplicate so that you can take a copy away with you. My secretary, Fr FitzHenry, will look after the recording. In case Fr Gaucher talks about "existential whitherness" I shall have with me my theologian, Mgr Bouverie, to act as interpreter. My Canon Lawyer, one Mgr Defew, will also be present.

If Fr Gaucher is to get an evening meal and catch the 9:15 plane to Rome from Heathrow, you will have to leave Stamford shortly after 5 p.m.

The copy of this last letter to Bishop Testastorta, along with a number of letters to nuns, was only delivered at Avignon on Easter Saturday, the eve of my departure for England. I filed them but did not have time to read them.

CHAPTER IX

MITRE AND CROOK

As Bishop Forester had warned me in his letter of March 12th, he was too busy to write to me again before Easter. Father FitzHenry continued to send copies of the Bishop's correspondence. He also confirmed that I was expected at Stamford for lunch on Tuesday, April 12th.

On Easter Sunday I said Mass for a pathetic little group of traditionalist "resisters" at Tarascon. Straight after Mass I started out for England. I did not fly, as Edmund had suggested, but drove. It is a long way, but, thanks to the motorways, I did it quite comfortably, spending Sunday night at Fontainebleau and Monday night in London. On Tuesday morning I drove to Stamford.

I was looking forward immensely to seeing Edmund. Not only was I very fond of him but my admiration for his stand was boundless. There was so much I wanted to hear from his own lips.

At 12:45 precisely I rang the bell at Bishop's House. Father FitzHenry opened the door. "Thank God you've come! He's dying. We rang you up on Sunday evening but could get no answer; you must already have left. I suppose you did not get the telegram either. He wants you to anoint him and give him Viaticum. . . . No, not immediately. He was in terrible pain on Sunday night but it seems to have worn off. He is in a sort of coma most of the time."

I went up to the bedroom. Defew and a nursing nun were there. Edmund appeared to be asleep. He had gone immensely thin. His complexion was ashen. "That's Bryan," he said without opening his eyes. "I knew you would be in time . . . always punctual." He opened his eyes, gradually turned his head towards me, and smiled. He said something else but his speech was not at all clear and I could not understand it. "He is asking for the Sacraments." Defew explained. Edmund nodded.

He was quite conscious while I administered the Sacraments. He said the Confiteor and even lisped the correct answers for Viaticum. FitzHenry asked me to have lunch with him and then relieve Defew afterwards.

According to FitzHenry, Edmund's collapse was due to his tour of the convents. "He is not dying of cancer but of exhaustion. Not only was the physical strain too much but the nervous tension broke him." On top of that, he had insisted on going to Horethorpe on Tuesday in Holy Week to talk to the young men he was ordaining on Sunday. The same afternoon he was closeted with Mother Crashaw at the Court for over an hour. On Thursday he celebrated the Mass of the Holy Oils. A whole crowd of clergy turned up; he was gay and kind to all. On Friday he attended the Mass of the Presanctified. "He was obviously feeling frightful. He sat throughout and had Holy Communion brought to him." He went to bed immediately afterwards and stayed there all Saturday, "in order to get through the Ordinations." This he did splendidly. The ceremony was magnificent. Defew had laid on Haydn's Missa Imperialis with full orchestra. There was not a hitch and Edmund performed "with the joyful solemnity of full conviction." His address to the ordinandi was simple and moving. He attended the lunch which had been arranged for them and their families, although he did not eat. He spoke to each parent. He did not get back to Bishop's House until after 3 p.m. "It was there that I found him huddled up on the sofa in his study, gently sobbing. He was in great pain. There was nobody in Bishop's House, so I asked a man in the street to help lift him up. I need not have bothered; he was as light as a feather. Luckily the doctor was at home and came round immediately. He gave him an injection to ease the pain. It was he who said that Edmund was not dying of cancer but of exhaustion. After the injection he stopped sobbing and went to sleep. Biggs called and got hold of Defew.

206

"He woke just after seven. It was then he said: 'Bryan's coming. I want him to give me the Last Rites and bury me.' He also asked to see Canon Cocksedge as soon as possible. . . ."

Cocksedge arrived at about 11 p.m. He was alone with Bishop Forester for nearly an hour. He drove back to Sandborough that night. After Cocksedge's visit, Edmund was again in pain. He did not sleep but was perfectly lucid. He was given another injection. He calmed down and started to sleep. He remained in much the same condition in which I had seen him. That is what I learned from Father FitzHenry.

I went up to the bedroom. Defew left to get some well-earned rest. Edmund opened his eyes, but I doubt if he could see properly. "Is that you, Bryan? I thought so. I want to thank you. I am so grateful, so grateful." There was a long pause. "I want you to trust Socks. He has explained everything. He has forgiven me. You will trust him, won't you?" He talked a good deal more but I could not understand most of it. The general gist was how happy he had been; how absurdly generous God is. Then he said quite clearly: "So I can die now." He went into a deep coma.

It was already about 5 p.m. The nurse brought me a cup of tea. She tried to wake Edmund but to no avail. "When he wakes, get him to drink something," she said.

It was shortly afterwards that he started repeating the Holy Name: "Jesu . . . Jesu . . . Jesu . . ." quite regularly, at the rate, I imagine, of about twice a minute, although he was completely unconscious. He came out of coma a couple of times, as though to make sure that I was still there. The first time he asked me: "Am I doing it right? One gets no practice at dying." He became unconscious again and continued repeating the Holy Name. The second time was shortly before his death. He became wide awake, recognized me, and smiled. He then said perfectly distinctly: "gloriabuntur qui diligunt nomen tuum" [They shall be glorified who love Thy Name, Ps.V]. I felt the end was near and rang the bell. Biggs, Defew, Bouverie and FitzHenry arrived. I gave Edmund the Last Blessing. He died at 5:15 a.m. on Wednesday morning, just before we finished reciting the Commendation for a Departing Soul.

After we had all said Mass for Edmund, the day began. It is fortunate that there is so much to be done after a death; it prevents fruitless nostalgia. It was decided to lay Edmund out in full pontificals on a catafalque at the foot of the altar steps in the Cathedral until midday Saturday, so that clergy and faithful could see him. On Saturday the body would be placed in a coffin and moved to the Holy Souls chapel in the south transept. The Requiem would take place at noon on Monday.

One of the difficulties was the shortage of telephones. FitzHenry would use that in Bishop's House to notify the press and deal with incoming calls. Biggs (the Vicar General) would go home—he lived at a convent the other end of the town— and notify relatives and personal friends. Defew would return to Cathedral House and notify the Chapter and diocesan clergy. I volunteered to go to St. Anthony's Presbytery in the town and deal with the Bishops and the Trust.

I first rang up Mr. Gote, the Trust's Secretary, to discover if the meeting fixed for 6 p.m. the following day could be postponed. For a variety of reasons it could not. He kindly offered to announce the death and confirm the meeting to the other Trustees. I then rang up the Bishops, starting with the Cardinal. Fortunately, in most cases I was able just to leave a message. I ended up with the Delegate, who was out and not expected back until late that evening.

I got back to Bishop's House in time for lunch. The undertakers had been there and had done their work thoroughly, including whatever is necessary to prevent the body from becoming objectionable. Edmund's own bedroom was too small and too untidy so they had laid him out, fully vested with mitre and crozier, in the large guest-room opposite. The curtains were drawn and the only light came from six tall tapers. They were due to call back that evening, when they had prepared the catafalque, to carry Edmund into the Cathedral.

What dignity death gives to people! In life Edmund was too kindly, too innocent, too happy to look dignified. His corpse spoke with an authority which his living frame had lacked. One was forced onto one's knees in his presence.

Actually, it was nearly 2 p.m. before we sat down to a cold lunch, Defew, Bouverie, FitzHenry and myself. Afterwards the admirable housekeeper brought us in a large jug of real coffee. We were still drinking it when there was a ring at the front door. Bouverie said, "I'll see who it is," and went out, leaving the door ajar. We could hear him from the dining-room. "Good afternoon, Bishop Testastorta. . . . Ah yes! Father Gaucher; I am delighted to meet you. My name is Charles Bouverie. Yes,

208

His Lordship is ready to receive you. I shall just get Mgr Defew and His Lordship's friend, Father Houghton."

FitzHenry looked at me. "I had completely forgotten him. Did you ring him up this morning?" "Yes, but he was out." As I have said, I had not read the copy of Edmund's letter of March 18th to Testastorta and was consequently unaware that he was expected.

Bouverie put his head round the door. "Bishop Testastorta and Father Gaucher have an appointment with His Lordship. Will you accompany them upstairs?" Bouverie led the way, followed by the visitors. FitzHenry, Defew and I formed up in the rear. Bouverie flung the door open. As I have said, the room was dark except for the feeble light of the tapers. There was a moment's hesitation while the eyes got used to the halflight. Opposite was a nun fingering her rosary. To the right lay Edmund, the flickering light reflecting on the gold of his mitre. He looked magnificent. Testastorta went to the bottom of the bed and flung himself on his knees. We followed suit. Gaucher remained standing. After a minute or so he said, "Look here, Testa, I didn't know you were bringing me to see a corpse. If we get back I may be able to catch an earlier plane."

"Wait for me downstairs," said Testastorta quite quietly. "I don't want to pray for this man but I want him to pray for me." Apart from the nun, he and I were left alone with Edmund. He did not hurry. When he got up, he turned to me. "I believe you were his most intimate friend. He was a wonderful man but too trusting, too trusting. His death is quite providential. A casuist of Gaucher's calibre could entangle an angel. I'll tell you: he wasn't going to tackle Forester about his famous Ad clerum at all but about a letter in which he said that he judged the Church's fallible practice in the light of her infallible Faith. You mustn't say that in our days. You invent the faith to suit the practice."

"You don't mean to say that Bishop Dobson forwarded that letter to you?" I asked, taken aback.

"No, not to me. Direct to Archbishop Klushko. But how do you come to know about it?"

"Edmund happened to send me a copy." I could see that I had fallen into a trap.

"Yes, of course he would. And who is the Bishop who will ordain his students now that he is dead?"

"How can I possibly tell?" I replied ambiguously and

209

added, to change the subject, "But I am surprised to hear about Bishop Dobson. Edmund was fond of him and trusted him absolutely."

"Too trusting. Well, there it is. I sometimes feel doubtful if I can trust myself. Anyway, I am glad that Bishop Forester has escaped from Gaucher's clutches. Quite providential. And it won't be difficult to discover the ordaining bishop."

"Perhaps the Cardinal," I suggested.

He knelt for another minute at Edmund's bedside and then went down to join Gaucher. They left immediately. I sat down beside poor Edmund. First Socks, and now Dobson: ambition and envy. Yes, he had been too trusting. I was too shaken to tell the others about the conversation.

The following day at 6 p.m. the Trust met in a boardroom at Messrs. Gote & Co's. The Duchess I had met a couple of times in Edmund's company. Bouverie I had met for the first time on Tuesday. The rest were unknown to me. We were subdued at Edmund's absence but very conscious that he had called us together precisely to continue his work.

Our first concern was to elect a clerical Trustee in place of Edmund. The obvious choice was Mgr Defew as President of the Association of St John Fisher. The Duchess rang him up to obtain his consent. He agreed. I learned that she had given a rambling building in Blackwater town to be the Association's headquarters—hostel, club, retreat house, what you will.

Some hundred priests from other dioceses had applied to join the Association. It was decided not to admit them until such time as there was a sufficient number in any one diocese to found a new branch of the Association, which the Trust could take under its wing.

Bouverie reported on Horethorpe. He had appointed the staff he wanted for September. He had managed to reconstitute the library from the old Seminary, which had been dispersed. Some money would be needed to bring it up to date.

Outman reported that the University would recognize the Teachers' Centre at Offleigh. It was to be run by a joint board representing the University and the Trust. The details of the agreement seemed eminently satisfactory. He spoke at some length about the diocesan schools. Anyway, he seemed perfectly happy.

Glauben gave details about finance. He had collected

some enormous sums of money, and added: "The death of Bishop Forester will double what we received in his life."

Negotiations were in progress with the Governors of Sockham College as with the owners of the Boys' Preparatory School. Mother Crashaw hoped to be able to open a Girls' Boarding School, etc. . . , etc.

I was astonished at how much had been done in so short a time. I had read about most of it in the letters, but it was quite a different matter to have it all summed up at one meeting as a set of concrete realities.

It was decided that the next meeting would be held as soon as possible after the appointment of the next bishop had been announced.

I came away confident that Edmund's work would not die with him.

I stayed at Bishop's House until Edmund's funeral to help FitzHenry sort his papers and generally to make myself useful.

Edmund's death had been announced on radio and television on Wednesday and was in all the papers on Thursday morning. His body had been brought down to the Cathedral on Wednesday evening. When the Cathedral opened at 6:30 a.m. on Thursday there was already a long queue of people waiting to pay homage to the Bishop, whose stand they understood. It must be remembered that Glauben's advertisement campaign had made Edmund a national figure. Opposition and defence in articles and interviews had swamped the mass media. In all this Edmund's opponents seemed to ordinary folk to have nothing to offer but incomprehensible jargon and legal quibbles. Edmund they could understand: it was a Bishop's job to talk about God and Jesus, Heaven and Hell. This is what he appeared to be doing. Moreover, he represented two ideas still dear to the British heart: tradition and fair play for the underdog. His supporters consequently were not only traditionalists, nor even the bulk of the Catholic laity, but the Great British Public. Anyway, from dawn to dusk each day, Thursday, Friday and Saturday, the queue never seemed to diminish. Coachloads brought them from all over the country. And the people cannot have gone away disappointed. As I have said, Edmund looked utterly magnificent: the ashen face, which breathed authority, between the golden mitre and the sumptuous vestments, with the flickering tapers and the praying priests and

211

nuns around him. It was difficult in front of him not to think of eternal life. Edmund may well have converted more people dead than living.

It was the same at his Requiem on Monday. Two or three times as many people stood outside in the drizzle as could be squeezed into the Cathedral. More priests were present than there are in the diocese of Stamford. Only bishops were lacking. Apart from four retired bishops, of whom three were missionaries, there was only the Cardinal, Archbishop Weir, Dobson and Testastorta. Mgr Defew arranged everything perfectly. It was solemn but not sad. So I laid my friend to rest.

Immediately after the funeral I returned to France. I could not stand the prospect of chatting to crowds of people. I wanted to be alone.

It was about six weeks later that the Duchess of Blackwater wrote to tell me that Canon Cocksedge had been appointed Bishop of Stamford. He was to be consecrated in the Cathedral by Testastorta on June 12th. He had written to her and asked particularly that the Trustees would attend the reception afterwards at Offleigh Country Club when he would outline his policy for the diocese. She asked me to turn up, as there would be a meeting of the Trust at Blackwater afterwards.

I went. The ceremony seemed to me quite frightful in spite of Defew's efforts to make the music at least respectable. On the other hand, the reception was well organized. There was a very long High Table for the Bishops and a few distinguished laity, among whom were the Duchess, Sir John and Lady Cutting, and Mr and Mrs Outman. The rest could sit where they liked at a crowd of small tables and help themselves from the buffet. Bouverie, Defew, Glauben, Villiers and myself squashed round a small one. In due course the toasts and speeches were served up. The Cardinal proposed the new Bishop's health in a few well-chosen words. This was seconded by the Provost in the name of the diocesan clergy. On the part of the laity Mr Outman, as Chairman of the County Council, said nothing with the utmost distinction. It was Socks's turn. After a conventional opening of thanks all round, he continued:

"But the person to whom my deepest thanks are due is not physically with us today. I refer, of course, to Edmund Forester. I am profoundly conscious of the difficulty of my position in having to succeed to a saint. Just look at what Edmund

212

Forester, a dying man, accomplished in the last three months of his life. Only a saint would have had the singleness of purpose and simplicity of mind to undertake what he undertook. Only a saint would have had the determination and humility to carry it through. Yes, I use the word 'humility' on purpose. Only the humble are capable of great actions. It is out of pride that most of us are so appallingly mediocre.

"But what is to happen to Edmund's work? It is in this connection that my diffidence in succeeding him is turned to confidence. This confidence does not arise from trust in my own ability but from my conviction that I shall be fulfilling the wishes of the Holy Father and of his Delegate, Bishop Testastorta, who has consecrated me your Bishop this day. It is, after all, a well-known fact that among Edmund's many friends very few, perhaps none, was more intimate than I. Not only was I his secretary in 1965 and 1966, but he made me a member of his Chapter so that he was at liberty to discuss with me the affairs of the diocese. When he wrote his now famous Ad clerum of January 13th, it was I whom he called to Bishop's House to help him put it into execution. When he lay dying, he asked to see two priests: his old friend Bryan Houghton—whom I am delighted to see with us today—and myself. It is therefore abundantly clear that if the Holy See has appointed me to be his successor it can only be in order to ensure that his work should be continued with the least possible interruption or alteration." He paused. There was a moment of amazed silence. Then the clapping and cheering broke out, arms waving, glasses crashing, people standing. When order was restored, Bishop Cocksedge continued.

"I am not the less grateful for your wonderful response for having expected it. I wish, however, to underline a few points in particular. Firstly, the Ad clerum of January 13th remains in force in this diocese. Secondly, the new Schools' Commission under Canon McCarthy will operate as Bishop Forester had intended. Thirdly, I shall work in close collaboration with the Trust, so ably and graciously chaired by the Duchess of Blackwater, notably over the seminary at Horethorpe and the Teachers' Centre at Offleigh. Lastly, I fully recognize the right of the diocesan clergy to join the Association of St John Fisher under the Presidency of Mgr Defew.

"That, I suspect, is as much as you wish to hear from me for the moment.

"The management has asked us to take coffee and brandy in the lounges in order to clear this hall."

The five of us at our table were too dumbfounded to speak, except for Glauben, who was weeping with laughter and muttering "Clown or crook, what a joke!"

As the High Table dispersed towards the lounges, the Duchess came across to us: "I think we can disappear decently in about half an hour, so I shall expect you all at Blackwater in just over an hour's time."

A little later in the lounge Testastorta came up to me. "I don't imagine you expected that," he said.

"No more than you," I answered. "The trouble with you, my dear Bishop, is that you are too trusting, too trusting."

He roared with merriment: "Yes, yes! When people lose the Faith they are automatically faithless. Everywhere are souls to save, but not a soul to trust. I hope we meet again. Pray for me."

We all arrived at Blackwater at much the same time so there was little backchat before the Duchess called us to order. "I suppose that I was the only person present," she said, "who knew what Cocksedge was going to say. That is why I so much wanted you to be present. I could not warn you as he had bound me to secrecy."

This is what Cocksedge had told her. Although not entirely in agreement with Edmund, he was overwhelmed with admiration for his stand in favour of the traditional forms of our religion. It was obvious, however, that Edmund's efforts were doomed to failure because he could not live long enough to see them through. At his death, the Holy See would only have to appoint a subservient bishop for all Edmund's work to be destroyed. He therefore determined to do all in his power to guarantee his own succession—even to the point of appearing to betray Edmund. He said that FitzHenry and myself would know to what he was referring. He had indeed obtained a promise of the succession out of Testastorta in return for keeping him informed of the attitude of Edmund's fellow bishops. However, he could not keep up this duplicity for long and returned to Sandborough as soon as he decently could. He had explained all this to Edmund on the Monday before his death. Edmund had believed him and had died in peace. Such was the outline of Cocksedge's story to the Duchess.

214

*None of us said a word. "You silence is very eloquent,"
the Duchess continued, "but not very helpful. We have got to
decide our attitude to the new Bishop. You, Father Houghton,
probably know him better than any of us, except, perhaps,
Monsignor Defew. What do you think?"*

*"It does not seem to me to matter if his story is true or
false," I replied. "That is his story and we must see that he
sticks to it. We are consequently the last people to deny it
although, maybe, the last to believe it. Let him save his face
so long as he saves the Faith."*

*"I heartily agree," said Mr Glauben. "That Cocksedge is a
crook I have not the slightest doubt. Having betrayed Forester,
he has betrayed Testa. But one can always trust a crook because
one knows his motives; it is honest fools one cannot because
one doesn't. We know Cocksedge's guiding principle:*

*I never back a horse
Which cannot stay the course*

*He has made up his mind that the revolution is no longer worth
backing—which, coming from so shrewd a man, must be a
great source of comfort to us all.*

*"Anyway, it is typical of Divine Providence. So that no
human should take to himself the glory, what God has initiated
through a saint He will bring to fruition through a crook."*

About the **Author**

BRYAN HOUGHTON (1911–1992), of Anglican background, was received into the Catholic Church in Paris in 1934 and ordained a priest on March 30, 1940. Throughout the 1960s he found himself increasingly at odds with the self-styled "reformers" who, in the name of Vatican II, were wreaking havoc in the Church. On the day the *Novus Ordo Missae* went into effect—November 29, 1969, the first Sunday of Advent—he resigned from his pastorship at Bury St Edmunds, refusing to celebrate with the new missal. Drawing on his inheritance, he purchased a property with a chapel in the region of Viviers in the south of France and, with his bishop's consent, continued to offer the Tridentine Mass for a small congregation until his death on November 19, 1992. He wrote two novels, *Mitre and Crook* and *Judith's Marriage*, a collection of essays, *Rejected Priest*, and a children's book, *Saint Edmund, King and Martyr*.

Ingram Content Group UK Ltd.
Milton Keynes UK
UKHW040744120423
420010UK00014B/83/J